PRENTICE HALL

ALGEBRA
TOOLS FOR A CHANGING WORLD

Chapter 1
Support File

Tools of Algebra

PRENTICE HALL
Upper Saddle River, New Jersey
Needham Heights, Massachusetts

ISBN: 0-13-433323-3

Printed in the United States of America
    8 9 10 11   02 01 00 99

Editorial, design, and production services: Publishers Resource Group, Inc.

PRENTICE HALL

Chapter 1

Tools of Algebra

Alternative Activity: Teacher's Notes for 1-1

Displaying Data Relationships with Graphs

TYPE OF ACTIVITY: Technology (Graphing calculator)

CONCEPTS: This Alternative Activity covers the same concepts as Example 3 Relating to the Real

World in the student text. Students use the graphing calculator to make a double line graph.

MATERIALS: Graphing calculator; Alternative Activity 1-1 student worksheet.

FACILITATING THE ACTIVITY

In this activity, students use a graphing calculator to draw the same graph that is shown in the text. This activity introduces students to the power of the graphing calculator.

The Data Table

ERROR ALERT! Students may read the table and forget to add the "billion." **Remediation:** Ask if 45 cans manufactured in a year is a reasonable number. Suggest that students always read the labels first when they are trying to understand the information in either a table or a graph.

The Simplified Data Tables

After students have completed Exercises 2–4, discuss with them how they might use a line graph to represent the data in the tables.

- Have students draw a coordinate system and identify the x-axis, the y-axis, and the origin.

- Have volunteers discuss the ranges they chose in Exercises 3 and 4. Have students label the axes using reasonable ranges.

The Graphing Calculator

The directions used in this lesson are specifically for the TI-82. Detailed instructions on how to perform various operations for several different calculators are given in the Graphing Calculator Handbook.

Have students turn on their calculators. Explain that the first step in making the graphs is to set the ranges and scales for the variables using WINDOW .

Possible settings are:

| Xmin=1989 | Xmax=1993 | Xscl=1 |
| Ymin=0 | Ymax=60 | Yscl=10 |

To draw the graph, begin by pressing the STAT key. Then press **1** to select EDIT. Use the arrow keys to move about in the lists as you type the data. Put Years in L_1, Manufactured in L_2, and Recycled in L_3. To plot this data, press 2nd [STAT PLOT]. Select Plot 1 by pressing **1**. *Select **On** and press ENTER . Use the arrow keys to move the cursor to the symbol for line graph (the second symbol) and press ENTER . Select L_1 for the **Xlist** and press ENTER . Select L_2 for the **Ylist** and press ENTER . Again press 2nd [STAT PLOT], select Plot 2 and press ENTER . Repeat all steps from *, but this time select L_3 for the **Ylist** and press ENTER . Press GRAPH to see the two lines. For this first exploration of the graphing calculator, have students draw the lines without adding any labels.

After completing the activity, turn off the plots. To do this, press 2nd [STAT PLOT] **4** ENTER .

ERROR ALERT! Students may try to enter 45,700,000,000 rather than 45.7. **Remediation:** Remind them that the label tells how large the number actually is so they may use the short form as they graph.

Alternative Activity: Student Worksheet for 1-1

Displaying Data Relationships with Graphs

RELATING TO THE REAL WORLD

The Data Table

What You'll Learn
Using a graphing calculator to graph the data in a table
What You'll Need
Graphing calculator

1. Make a generalization about the number of cans manufactured compared to the number of cans recycled.

Aluminum Soft Drink Cans (in billions)

Year	Manufactured	Recycled
1989	45.7	27.8
1990	49.2	31.3
1991	53.0	33.0
1992	54.9	37.3
1993	58.0	36.6

Source: Can Manufacturing Institute

The Simplified Data Tables

2. Fill in the data in these two tables. The left column of each table represents the x-coordinate (years), and the right column represents the y-coordinate (cans).

Manufactured	(in billions)
1989	
1990	
1991	
1992	
1993	

Recycled	
1989	
1990	
1991	
1992	
1993	

3. Write a reasonable range for the horizontal axis or x-axis (years).

4. Write a reasonable range for the vertical axis or y-axis (cans).

The Graphing Calculator

Use your graphing calculator to draw a double line graph (one line for each table) for the data.

5. Compare the trends of the two lines. Do the two lines intersect?

6. Explain what would have to happen in order for the two lines to intersect.

Alternative Activity: Teacher's Notes for 1-4

Adding and Subtracting Integers

TYPE OF ACTIVITY: Manipulative

CONCEPTS: This Alternative Activity covers the same concepts as Example 2 of the student lesson. Instead of algebra tiles, it uses a variation of the number line to help students discover the Subtraction Rule.

MATERIALS: Alternative Activity 1-4 student worksheet; place markers such as paper clips

---

FACILITATING THE ACTIVITY

This activity expands the analogy between football plays and the number line that was suggested in Example 1 Relating to the Real World.

Exercises 1–2

These first two questions encourage students to look at the diagram and to check their understanding of the situation pictured.

Exercise 3

Students who learn best kinesthetically will benefit from using lines marked on the floor with masking tape, moving to the right and left to show yards gained and lost.

Ask students:

- *What type of integer could represent a gain in yardage?* **positive**

- *What type of integer could represent a loss in yardage?* **negative**

Exercise 4

Discuss how running away from your opponent's goal might be represented. **adding a negative integer or subtracting a positive integer** Discuss how running away from your team's goal might be represented. **adding a positive integer or subtracting a negative integer**

Exercises 5–7

Before they begin to find the results, suggest that students tell their partners about a football play that could be represented by each expression.

Exercise 8

ERROR ALERT! Students may not see the relationship between the pairs of problems.

Remediation: Ask students: *In what ways are the two problems in Exercise 5 alike? How are they different?* **The absolute values of the integers are alike. The operations are different and the sign of the second integer is different.**

Guide students to discover the pattern for themselves. Later in the text, they will read the formal statement of the Subtraction Rule. Encourage students to think through the problems step by step and let the rule present itself instead of waiting for the teacher to present the rule.

Alternative Activity: Student Worksheet for 1-4
Adding and Subtracting Integers

Work with a partner. Use the diagram of a football field to answer the following questions.

> **What You'll Learn**
> Subtracting integers
>
> **What You'll Need**
> A place marker such as a paper clip

1. How far is it from one dotted line to the next?

2. In football, the team tries to move the ball toward their opponent's goal. If your team gains yardage on a play, which way does the ball move on the diagram?

The S on the diagram marks the starting position of the ball. Place a marker on the S. Your first play results in a gain of 3 yd. Move the marker to the right to show the gain. Your second play results in a loss of 8 yd. Move the marker to the left to show the loss.

Part of a Football Field

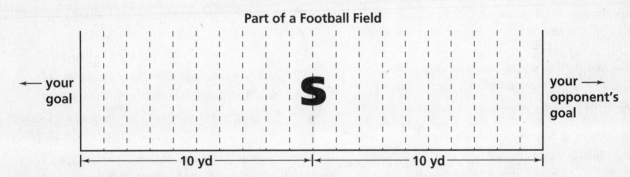

← your goal

your → opponent's goal

|← 10 yd →|← 10 yd →|

3. Describe your team's position in relation to S.

The expression $3 - 8$ represents the two plays mathematically. You first gained 3 yd and then lost 8 yd. The result is that your team lost 5 yd (or moved 5 yd to the left of S).

The equation $3 - 8 = -5$ represents the result mathematically.

Start over at S. With your first play, you gain 5 yd. On your second play, you lose 9 yd. Decide where to move the marker to show the two plays.

4. Write a mathematical equation that represents the result.

Start over at S. Your player runs toward your opponent's goal for 4 yd (move the marker) and then *runs away from your team's goal* for 5 yd (move the marker again). There are two ways to represent this with a mathematical equation: $4 - (-5) = 9$ or $4 + 5 = 9$.

Use the diagram to find each difference or sum.

5. **a.** $3 - 7$
   b. $3 + (-7)$

6. **a.** $4 - (-6)$
   b. $4 + 6$

7. **a.** $-2 - 5$
   b. $-2 + (-5)$

8. Look for a pattern in Exercises 5–7. Complete this sentence in your own words: Subtracting a number can be written as adding _____?

Alternative Activity: Teacher's Notes for 1-7

Experimental Probability and Simulations

TYPE OF ACTIVITY: Technology (Graphing calculator or software with random number generator)

CONCEPTS: This Alternative Activity covers the same concepts as Part 2 Conducting a Simulation (including Example 2) in the student text. Students generate random numbers to conduct a simulation.

MATERIALS: Graphing calculator (or software with a random number generator); Alternative Activity 1-7 student worksheet

---

FACILITATING THE ACTIVITY

This activity takes students through two simulations. For finding experimental probabilities, simulations are usually faster and more cost-effective than actual experiments. Students conduct their own simulations by using the random number generator found in a graphing calculator or computer software. The information that follows details how to access the random number generators in several graphing calculators.

Generating Random Numbers

Press `MATH` `◄` `ENTER` . The word *rand* will appear on the screen. Press `ENTER` and a random number from 0 to 1 will appear. A sample is .9641810947.

Once the calculator is in the random generator mode, it will continue to produce random digits each time `ENTER` is pressed. *Zeros before the decimal point are placeholders and should be ignored.* A truncated display (fewer than ten digits) indicates that a random digit of 0 has been generated but not displayed.

Number Cube Simulation

Once random digits are available, the student must assign proper roles to the digits. In this simulation, only six digits are needed, corresponding to the six surfaces of the number cube. The remaining digits are discarded.

Ask students to find the probability of getting a sum of 7 based on the seven trials shown in the sample work. $\frac{1}{7}$, **since one trial out of seven is a success**.

Ask students to list the advantages and disadvantages of a simulation compared to an actual experiment. **Simulation is faster and easier. Sometimes an actual experiment can be quite expensive**.

Kicking Simulation

Statisticians and other researchers carefully define success and failure before they gather data, to avoid being influenced by the data. Here, students should assign four specific digits to represent failure and three others to represent success before they conduct the simulation.

Alternative Activity: Student Worksheet **for 1-7**
Experimental Probability and Simulations

NUMBER CUBE SIMULATION

A simulation is a model that allows you to predict what might happen in a real-life situation. Suppose you want to know the probability of getting a sum of 7 when you roll two number cubes. You can simulate this problem by using random numbers.

> **What You'll Learn**
> Using simulations to find experimental probability
>
> **What You'll Need**
> Graphing calculator or software with a random number generator

Step 1. Define how the simulation will be done.

- Use a graphing calculator or software to generate random numbers.

  1 8 4 8 9 4 2 3 0 2 5 5 6 8 5 7 1 6 5 3

- Since a number cube has only the digits 1–6, discard each 7, 8, 9, or 0.

  1 8 4 8 9 4 2 3 0 2 5 5 6 8 5 7 1 6 5 3

- To represent two number cubes, pair the remaining digits.

  14   42   32   55   65   16   53

- Find each sum. Conduct 50 trials.

  5   6   5   10   11   7   8

Step 2. Conduct the simulation.

Generate random numbers and follow the procedure above until you have 50 trials.

Step 3. Interpret the simulation.

_____ out of 50 trials represent a sum of 7.

$P(\text{sum of 7}) = \dfrac{\text{number of favorable outcomes}}{\text{number of trials}} = \dfrac{}{50}$

KICKING SIMULATION

Suppose the best kicker for your school's soccer team makes three out of every seven penalty kicks she tries. In a typical game she makes three attempts. What is the probability that the next time she has three attempts in a game, she will make all three?

1. Design a simulation similar to the one above. (Hint: Assign three specific digits to represent success and four to represent failure.)

2. Conduct the simulation.

3. Interpret the simulation.

Reteaching 1-1

• •

OBJECTIVE: Drawing and interpreting graphs   **MATERIALS:** Graph paper for each student

Example

Use the graph to answer the questions.

1. What kind of graph is this and why was this kind chosen? This is a line graph, which was chosen because it shows change over time.

2. What is the vertical scale? The scale is $10,000 to $32,500 with every $5000 labeled.

3. What is the horizontal scale? The scale is 1991 to 1996 with every year labeled and each quarter marked.

4. What trend do you see? In general, the dollar value of the investment increases during the time period shown.

Growth of a $10,000 Investment in a Mutual Fund

Source: *Time* Magazine

Activity

Use the data in the table to answer the questions and draw a graph.

Total Government Employees (in thousands)

Year	Employees	Year	Employees
1940	4474	1960	8808
1945	6677	1965	10,589
1950	6402	1970	13,028
1955	7432	1975	14,973

Source: *Information Please Almanac*

1. What kind of graph best suits the data? Why?

2. What is a reasonable vertical scale?

3. What is a reasonable horizontal scale?

4. Draw the graph.

5. Describe any trend that occurs.

Reteaching 1-2

• •

> **OBJECTIVE:** Using variables as a shorthand way to express relationships
>
> **MATERIALS:** None

You often hear word phrases such as *half as much* or *three times as deep*. These phrases describe mathematical relationships. You can translate word phrases like these into mathematical relationships called *equations*.

Example

Translate the following word expression into an equation.

The weight of the truck is two times the weight of the car.

$$=$$

⟵ **If the written expression contains the word *is* or *equals*, then the mathematical expression will be an equation. Write the equal sign for the equation under the word *is*.**

The weight of the truck is two times the weight of the car.

$$t \quad = 2 \quad \cdot \quad c$$

⟵ **Whatever is written to the left of *is* will be placed on the left side of the =. Whatever is written to the right side of *is* will be placed on the right side of the =. Represent the unknown amounts with variables.**

$$t = 2c$$

⟵ **The translation is complete. Check to make sure you have translated all parts of the equation.**

Activity

Translate the following word expressions into equations. Make sure you translate all parts of the word expressions.

1. Four quarts are equal to one gallon.

2. A touchdown is equal to six points.

3. Mei Ling is two inches taller than Paulo.

4. The mass of Jupiter is 317.8 times the mass of the earth.

Reteaching 1-3

OBJECTIVE: Using the order of operations	**MATERIALS:** Three index cards or small pieces of paper

Review the order of operations to help you with this activity.

> **Order of Operations**
> 1. Perform any operations inside grouping symbols.
> 2. Simplify any term with exponents.
> 3. Multiply and divide in order from left to right.
> 4. Add and subtract in order from left to right.

Example

Write $+$ on the first index card, $-$ on the second card, and $\times$ on the third card. Shuffle the cards and place them face down on your desk. Pick cards at random to fill in the blanks with operation signs. Once you have filled in the operation signs, simplify the expression.

6____(9____7)____8	⟵ **Pick cards to fill in the blanks with operation signs.**
$6 \cdot (9 - 7) + 8$	⟵ **Subtract 7 from 9 inside the grouping symbols.**
$6 \cdot 2 + 8$	⟵ **Do multiplication and division first. Multiply 6 by 2.**
$12 + 8$	⟵ **Do addition and subtraction last. Add 12 and 8 to get the answer.**
20	⟵ **The answer is 20.**

Activity

Pick cards at random to fill in the operation symbols of the following expressions. Simplify the expressions.

1. 7_____ 5_____ 1

2. (3_____ 9)_____ 4

3. 8_____ 2_____ (5_____ 10)

4. (3_____ 7_____ 6)_____1

Additional Exercises

Solve each expression by following the order of operations.

5. $(5 \cdot 3) - 18$

6. $2 \cdot (27 - 13 \cdot 2)$

7. $18 \div (9 - 15 \div 5)$

8. $2 \cdot 8 - 6^2$

Reteaching 1-4

· ·

OBJECTIVE: Adding and subtracting with integers and decimals   **MATERIALS:** None

Review the following addition and subtraction rules.

· To add two numbers with the same sign, *add* their absolute values. The sum has the same sign as the numbers.

· To add two numbers with different signs, find the *difference* of their absolute values. The sum has the same sign as the number with the greater absolute value.

· To subtract a number, add its opposite.

Example

The following example shows you step-by-step how to add two numbers with different signs.

$$-6 + 2$$

$$\left|-6\right| - \left|2\right|$$ ⟵ **Rewrite this problem as the difference of the absolute values.**

$$6 - 2$$

$$4$$ ⟵ **Subtract.**

$$-4$$ ⟵ **Since −6 has the greater absolute value, the answer takes the negative sign.**

Activity

Find the sum or difference for each problem. Be sure to check the sign of your answer.

1. $-3 + (-4)$ **2.** $12 + 5$ **3.** $5 - 8$ **4.** $-8 + (-2)$

5. $-2 - (-3)$ **6.** $9 + (-12)$ **7.** $-3 - 5$ **8.** $-4 + 3$

Additional Exercises

Evaluate each expression for $a = 5$ and $b = -4$.

9. $-a - b$ **10.** $-a + b$ **11.** $a + b$ **12.** $a - b$

Reteaching 1-5

· ·

> **OBJECTIVE:** Multiplying and dividing with integers and decimals
>
> **MATERIALS:** A number cube

Review the following multiplication and division rules.

- The product or quotient of two positive numbers is positive.
- The product or quotient of two negative numbers is positive.
- The product or quotient of a positive and a negative number is negative.

Example

Roll the number cube to determine the signs of the numbers in the following problem. If you roll an even number (2, 4, or 6), write $+$ in the blank to make the number positive. If you roll an odd number (1, 3, or 5), write a $-$ in the blank to make the number negative. Decide what sign the answer will be before you calculate the answer.

____ 56 ÷ ____ 7   ⟵   **Roll the number cube to fill in the blanks.**

$-56 \div (+7)$ ⟵   **Suppose your first roll was a 3, so 56 is negative. Suppose your second roll was 6, so 7 is positive. Now that you have the signs of the numbers, decide what the sign of the answer will be. Dividing a positive number by a negative number results in a negative number.**

-8 ⟵   **The answer is -8.**

Activity

Roll the number cube to determine the signs of the numbers in the following exercises. Remember to decide what sign the answer will be before you calculate the answer.

1. ____ 20 · ____ 8

2. ____ 3.2 · ____ 10

3. ____ 27 ÷ ____ 3

4. ____ 14 · ____ 4

5. ____ 120 ÷ ____ 12

6. ____ 45 ÷ ____ 9

7. ____ 1.4 · ____ 3

8. ____ 96 ÷ ____ 8

Reteaching 1-6

OBJECTIVE: Evaluating expressions with rational numbers

MATERIALS: A number cube

A rational number is any number you can write in the form of a fraction. The following example will show you how to evaluate expressions with rational numbers.

Example

Roll a number cube to choose denominators and numerators for the rational numbers. Then evaluate the expression by substituting.

Evaluate $2q + 3r$ where $q = \frac{n_1}{d}$ and $r = \frac{n_2}{d}$

Evaluate $2q + 3r$ where $q = \frac{n_1}{3}$ and $r = \frac{n_2}{3}$ ⟵ **Roll the number cube once. Replace d in both rational numbers with the number you rolled. Suppose you rolled a 3.**

Evaluate $2q + 3r$ where $q = \frac{2}{3}$ and $r = \frac{1}{3}$ ⟵ **Replace n_1 with the second number you roll. Replace n_2 with the third number you roll. Suppose you rolled a 2 and a 1.**

$$2\left(\frac{2}{3}\right) + 3\left(\frac{1}{3}\right)$$ ⟵ **Substitute the values for q and r.**

$$\frac{4}{3} + \frac{3}{3}$$ ⟵ **Multiply.**

$$\frac{7}{3}$$ ⟵ **Add.**

$$2\frac{1}{3}$$ ⟵ **Write the improper fraction as a mixed number.**

Activity

Roll the number cube to pick d, n_1, and n_2 for the rational numbers. Then evaluate the expressions by substituting.

1. $a - (-2b)$ for $a = \frac{n_1}{d}$ and $b = \frac{n_2}{d}$

2. $4j + 10k$ for $j = \frac{n_1}{d}$ and $k = \frac{n_2}{d}$

3. $\frac{1}{2}c + \frac{3}{2}d$ for $c = \frac{n_1}{d}$ and $d = \frac{n_2}{d}$

4. $3xy$ for $x = \frac{n_1}{d}$ and $y = \frac{n_2}{d}$

Reteaching 1-7

OBJECTIVE: Finding experimental probability	**MATERIALS:** Four index cards

The experimental probability of an event is the number of times the event happens divided by the number of times the experiement is done.

The following example will demonstrate how to calculate experimental probability with real data.

Example

Julie and Omar drew a square on one index card, a circle on a second index card, and a triangle on a third index card. Omar held the cards and let Julie draw one at random, without looking at them. They recorded which card Julie drew. Omar then replaced the card, shuffled, and let Julie draw again. They repeated this process 10 times. In the end, Julie drew the circle card 2 times, the square card 5 times, and the triangle card 3 times. What is the experimental probability of Julie drawing a circle card?

$$P(\text{event}) = \frac{\text{number of times an event happens}}{\text{number of times the experiment is done}}$$

$P(\text{of drawing a circle card}) = \frac{2}{10}$ ⟵   **Substitute the number of times Julie drew a circle card for the number of times the event happens. Substitute the total number of cards Julie drew for the number of times the experiment was done.**

$= \frac{1}{5} = 20\%$ ⟵   **In the experiment, Julie had a 1 out of 5, or 20%, chance of drawing a circle card.**

Activity

Repeat the above experiment with a partner. For your experiment, add a fourth card with a star drawn on it. Use the data you gather to fill in the following table. After you have finished, repeat the experiment for 20 trials. How does the experimental probability change?

Type of card	Times the card was drawn	Experimental probability as a percent
1. Square		
2. Circle		
3. Triangle		
4. Star		

Reteaching 1-8

OBJECTIVE: Adding and subtracting matricies   **MATERIALS:** None

To add or subtract matrices of the same size, draw arrows connecting the corresponding entries and their results. The following example illustrates how.

Example

Add the two matricies.

$\begin{bmatrix} 2 & 3 \\ 1 & 0 \end{bmatrix} + \begin{bmatrix} 4 & 7 \\ -5 & 8 \end{bmatrix} = \begin{bmatrix} & \\ & \end{bmatrix}$ ⟵ **Add the corresponding entries.**

$\begin{bmatrix} 2 & 3 \\ 1 & 0 \end{bmatrix} + \begin{bmatrix} 4 & 7 \\ -5 & 8 \end{bmatrix} = \begin{bmatrix} 6 & \\ & \end{bmatrix}$ ⟵ **2 + 4 = 6**

$\begin{bmatrix} 2 & 3 \\ 1 & 0 \end{bmatrix} + \begin{bmatrix} 4 & 7 \\ -5 & 8 \end{bmatrix} = \begin{bmatrix} 6 & 10 \\ & \end{bmatrix}$ ⟵ **3 + 7 = 10**

$\begin{bmatrix} 2 & 3 \\ 1 & 0 \end{bmatrix} + \begin{bmatrix} 4 & 7 \\ -5 & 8 \end{bmatrix} = \begin{bmatrix} 6 & 10 \\ -4 & \end{bmatrix}$ ⟵ **1 + (−5) = −4**

$\begin{bmatrix} 2 & 3 \\ 1 & 0 \end{bmatrix} + \begin{bmatrix} 4 & 7 \\ -5 & 8 \end{bmatrix} = \begin{bmatrix} 6 & 10 \\ -4 & 8 \end{bmatrix}$ ⟵ **0 + 8 = 8**

Activity

Draw arrows connecting the corresponding entries. Add or subtract the following matricies.

1. $\begin{bmatrix} 2 & 5 \\ 7 & -2 \end{bmatrix} + \begin{bmatrix} -4 & -2 \\ -1 & 3 \end{bmatrix}$ **2.** $\begin{bmatrix} 6 & 8 \\ 11 & 2 \end{bmatrix} - \begin{bmatrix} -2 & -7 \\ -1 & -1 \end{bmatrix}$

3. $\begin{bmatrix} 6 & 1 & 7 \\ 3 & 2 & -5 \end{bmatrix} + \begin{bmatrix} -8 & 6 & -2 \\ 14 & -3 & 1 \end{bmatrix}$ **4.** $\begin{bmatrix} 2.5 & 3.1 \\ 9.7 & 8.2 \end{bmatrix} + \begin{bmatrix} 6.4 & -3.3 \\ -2.6 & 1.9 \end{bmatrix}$

5. $\begin{bmatrix} -8 \\ -6 \\ 9 \end{bmatrix} - \begin{bmatrix} 4 \\ 5 \\ -1 \end{bmatrix}$ **6.** $\begin{bmatrix} 2 & 4 & 0 \\ -6 & 7 & 3 \\ 9 & -1 & 1 \end{bmatrix} - \begin{bmatrix} 1 & -2 & 3 \\ 9 & -6 & 8 \\ 4 & 7 & 0 \end{bmatrix}$

Reteaching 1-9

• •

OBJECTIVE: Using variables and formulas in a spreadsheet	**MATERIALS:** None

Spreadsheet Operation Symbols

Multiplication:	*	Example:	$2 \cdot 3$ is 2*3
Division:	/	Example:	$8 \div 4$ is 8/4
Raise to a power:	^	Example:	6^2 is 6^2

Spreadsheets organize data and functions into rows and columns. In spreadsheets, numbers or functions are stored in cells. A cell is named after the column and row in which it falls. For example, a cell in column D and row 3 would be called D3. In spreadsheets, cell names are often used for variables instead of letters such as x or y. Read through the following example to see how to evaluate expressions in spreadsheets.

Example

Write the formula and find the value for cell B2.

	A	B	C	D
1	x	$x + 3$	$2x - 2$	x^2
2	-3			
3	7			

Look at row 1 in the spreadsheet above. The cells in row 1 describe the expressions that you will use to calculate the values for the cells in the rows below row 1. For example, the value in cell A1 is x and the value in cell B1 is $x + 3$. To find the actual value in cell B1, you take the value in cell A1 and add 3 (B1=A1+3). Now look at row 2. The value in cell A2 is -3. To find the value for cell B2, take the value in cell A2 (-3) and add 3 (B2=A2+3).

$$B2 = A2 + 3 \quad \longleftarrow \textbf{ Write the formula.}$$

$$B2 = -3 + 3 \quad \longleftarrow \textbf{ Substitute for variables.}$$

$$B2 = 0 \quad \longleftarrow \textbf{ Calculate the answer.}$$

Activity

Calculate the value in each cell from the spreadsheet above.

1. cell C2   **2.** cell D2   **3.** cell B3   **4.** cell C3   **5.** cell D3

Practice 1-1

· ·

Example Exercises

Example 1

Find the mean for each set of data. Round to the nearest tenth.

1. 0, 5, 5, 10

2. 2, 9, 7, 3, 9, 4, 9, 8, 3, 2

3. 2.7, 5.6, 8.1, 10.9, 12.7, 9.5

4. 5.5, 5.8, 6.2, 6.4, 5.9, 6.1

5. 9, 10, 10, 11, 12

6. 10, 12, 13, 9, 4, 8, 7, 9, 15

Find the median for each set of data.

7. 1, 4, 6, 9, 12

8. 6.3, 12.2, 9.5, 3.1, 4.8

9. 2, 6, 8, 10

10. 11.8, 8.2, 3.8, 9.6, 8.9

11. 3, 9, 5, 7, 4, 7

12. 2, 12, 8, 7, 3, 8, 2, 5, 9

Find the mode for each set of data.

13. 6, 4, 8, 2, 4, 7

14. 2, 5, 8, 2, 3, 8, 4

15. 9, 7, 8, 9, 10, 9, 8, 10

16. 2.8, 7.4, 4.8, 2.8, 6.4, 7.1

17. 3, 8, 2, 9, 10, 4, 6, 12, 15

18. 6.4, 7.5, 9.8, 3.9, 7.5, 8.3

Example 2

Draw a multiple bar graph for the table.

19. **Population of the Three Largest U.S. Cities
(rounded to the nearest hundred thousand)**

City	1970	1980	1990
New York	7,900,000	7,100,000	7,300,000
Los Angeles	2,800,000	3,000,000	3,500,000
Chicago	3,400,000	3,000,000	2,800,000

Source: Bureau of the Census, U.S. Dept. of Commerce

20. Which cities showed a decrease in population between 1970 and 1980?

21. What city showed both an increase and a decrease?

Example 3

Draw a double line graph for the table.

22. **Technology in Public Schools**

Year	Interactive Video	Modems
1992	6502	13,597
1993	11,729	18,471
1994	17,489	22,611

Source: Quality Education Data, Inc.

23. Which technology showed the smaller increase from 1992 to 1994?

24. What trend do you see in the number of schools with modems?

· ·

Practice 1-1
Mixed Exercises

Find the mean for the following data. Round to the nearest tenth.

1. 8, 1, 2, 9, 5

2. 2.1, 9.2, 6.4, 7.3, 10.3, 9.6

3. 3.3, 7.2, 6.3, 8.3, 9, 12, 4, 5.6

Draw a multiple bar graph for the table.

4.

Population of States
(rounded to the nearest hundred thousand)

State	1960	1970	1980	1990
Arkansas	1,800,000	1,900,000	2,300,000	2,400,000
Indiana	4,700,000	5,200,000	5,500,000	5,500,000
Michigan	7,800,000	8,900,000	9,300,000	9,300,000
New Jersey	6,100,000	7,200,000	7,400,000	7,700,000

Source: Bureau of the Census, U.S. Dept. of Commerce

5. What happened to Indiana's population during these years?

6. Which state had the greatest increase in population?

Find the median for the following data.

7. 3, 9, 2, 7, 5

8. 3, 8, 4, 0, 1, 6, 7

9. 89, 94, 96, 86, 93, 95, 89, 92

10. 9.25, 10.75, 8.25, 7.50, 6.25

11. 16.4, 19.7, 13.4, 9, 12

12. 8, 9, 12, 17, 12, 13, 9, 6, 4, 12

Draw a double line graph for the table.

13.

Life Expectancy at Birth

Year	Male	Female
1940	60.8	65.2
1950	65.6	71.1
1960	66.6	73.1
1970	67.1	74.7
1980	70.0	77.5
1990	71.8	78.8

Source: National Center for Health Statistics

14. What is the trend for the life expectancy of males and females?

15. Which group's life expectancy has increased more, males or females?

16. During which decade did life expectancy increase most?

Find the mode for the following data.

17. 97, 84, 85, 93, 85, 92

18. 11, 16, 13, 18, 19, 17, 12

19. 9.1, 9.5, 9.4, 9.8, 9.2, 9.5

Find the mean for the following data. Round to the nearest tenth.

20. 5.6, 8.3, 9.1, 2.4, 1.8

21. 0.5, 1.4, 6.2, 4.8

22. 19, 17, 12, 15, 16, 18, 18, 11

23. 5, 6, 7, 8, 8, 7, 6, 5

24. 92, 91, 84, 86, 87, 91, 75, 73, 91, 85, 87, 81

Practice 1-2
Example Exercises

Example 1

In Excercises 1-5, use an equation to model each situation.

1. The total cost equals the number of bottles times $1.95.

2. The total amount of money earned is the number of hours worked times $6.50.

3. The amount of money in a bag of nickels is the number of nickels times $.05.

4. The cost of buying 10 gal of gas is 10 times the price per gallon.

5. What is the total cost of renting several videos at $2.50 each?

6. The equation for the total cost of buying tickets to a movie at $3.50 per ticket is $c = 3.50t$.

   a. What do the variables c and t represent?

   b. Write the equation that you would use when the price of tickets is raised to $4.00.

   c. Suppose the equation for the total cost of tickets is $c = 3.25t$. What does this mean?

7. Your teacher wants you to write the equation that could be used to find the total cost of bananas at 0.39 per pound. You write $c = 0.39n$ and Maria writes $b = 0.39p$. Explain why both equations are correct.

Example 2

Use an equation to model the relationship in each table.

8.

Tickets	Cost
2	$7
4	$14
6	$21
8	$28

9.

Hours	Distance
1	55 mi
3	165 mi
5	275 mi
7	385 mi

10.

Hours	Pay
8	$40
12	$60
16	$80
20	$100

11.

Cost	Change
$10.00	$0
$9.00	$1.00
$7.50	$2.50
$5.00	$5.00

12.

Days	Length
1	0.45 in.
4	1.80 in.
8	3.60 in.
10	4.50 in.

13.

Miles Traveled	Miles Remaining
0	500
125	375
350	150

Practice 1-2

· ·

Mixed Exercises

Use an equation to model each situation.

1. How does the amount of money in five-dollar bills relate to the number of five-dollar bills?

2. What is the total cost of buying several shirts that are $24.95 each?

3.
Tapes	Cost
1	$7.50
2	$15.00
3	$22.50
4	$30.00

4.
Hours	Pay
4	$28
6	$42
8	$56
10	$70

5.
Miles Hiked	Miles To Go
1.5	3.5
2.5	2.5
5.0	0

6. The number of gallons of water used to water trees is 30 times the number of trees.

7. What is the amount of money in a bank containing only dimes?

8. What is the number of marbles left from a 48-piece bag after some have been given away?

9.
Gallons	Miles
3	75
5	125
7	175
9	225

10.
Cost	Change
$15.00	$0
$12.00	$3.00
$11.50	$3.50
$10.21	$4.79

11.
Books	Cost
1	$3.50
2	$7.00
3	$10.50
4	$14.00

12. The total cost equals the price of the tickets times eight people.

13. What is the cost of buying several pairs of pants at $32.95 a pair?

14.
Days	Hours
2	48
4	96
7	168
11	264

15.
Weeks	Length
1	1.25 cm
3	3.75 cm
5	6.25 cm
7	8.75 cm

16.
Tickets Sold	Empty Seats
100	150
230	20
250	0

17.
Sales	Profits
$10	$3
$20	$6
$30	$9
$40	$12

18.
Apples Eaten	Apples Remaining
3	21
7	17
12	12

19.
Years	Months
1	12
2	24
6	72
10	120

20. The equation for the total cost of buying gasoline at $1.20/gal is $c = 1.20g$.

   a. What do the variables c and g represent?

   b. Write the equation for the total cost of gasoline at $1.25/gal.

Practice 1-3
· ·
Example Exercises

Example 1

Use the expression $p + r \times p$ to calculate the total cost of the following.

1. A jacket costs $39.95 with a sales tax rate of 7%. What is the total cost of the jacket?

2. A CD player costs $129.95 with a sales tax rate of 8%. What is the total cost of the CD player?

Example 2

Simplify each expression.

3. $6 \times 2 - 4$ 　　　4. $8 + 12 \div 3$ 　　　5. $2 \times 5 + 3 \times 4$

Evaluate each expression for $a = 3$ and $b = 4$.

6. $7b - 6a$ 　　　7. $12a + 5b$ 　　　8. $6b \div 4a$

9. $a + 3b$ 　　　10. $4a - 6 + 3b$ 　　　11. $8 - b + 2a$

Evaluate each expression for $m = 8$ and $n = 2$.

12. $2m - 3n$ 　　　13. $5m + 7n - 12$ 　　　14. $6m - 4n \div 8$

15. $m + 2n$ 　　　16. $12 \div n + 12m$ 　　　17. $3m - 8n$

18. Thuy evaluated the expression $3m - 2n \div 3$ for $m = 6$ and $n = 6$. Her result was 2. Is this answer correct? If not, what error did she make?

Example 3

Evaluate each expression for $x = 11$ and $y = 8$.

19. $(x + y)^2$ 　　　20. $x^2 + y^2$ 　　　21. xy^2 　　　22. $(xy)^2$

Example 4

Simplify each expression.

23. $\dfrac{8 + 4}{7 - 3}$ 　　　24. $\dfrac{2(4 + 1)}{4 - 2}$ 　　　25. $25\left(\dfrac{6 + 8}{2}\right)$

Evaluate the following for $x = 4$, $y = 8$, and $z = 12$.

26. $\dfrac{3x + y}{10}$ 　　　27. $\dfrac{y + z}{x}$ 　　　28. $\dfrac{4(x + y)}{2z}$

· ·

Practice 1-3

• •

Mixed Exercises

Simplify each expression.

1. $4 + 6(8)$

2. $\frac{4(8 - 2)}{3 + 9}$

3. $21 \times 3 + 2$

4. $40 \div 5(2)$

5. $2.7 + 3.6 \times 4.5$

6. $3[4(8 - 2) + 5]$

7. $4 + 3(5 - 2)$

8. $17 - [(3 + 2) \times 2]$

9. $6 \times (3 + 2) \div 15$

Evaluate each expression.

10. $\frac{a + 2b}{5}$ for $a = 1$ and $b = 2$

11. $\frac{5m + n}{5}$ for $m = 6$ and $n = 15$

12. $x + 3y$ for $x = 3.4$ and $y = 3$

13. $7a - 4(b + 2)$ for $a = 5$ and $b = 2$

Simplify each expression.

14. $\frac{100 - 15}{9 + 8}$

15. $\frac{2(3 + 4)}{7}$

16. $\frac{3(4 + 12)}{2(7 - 3)}$

17. $14 + 3 \times 4$

18. $8 + 3(4 + 3)$

19. $3 + 4[13 - 2(6 - 3)]$

20. $8(5 + 30 \div 5)$

21. $(3.4)(2.7) + 5$

22. $50 \div 2 + 15 \times 4$

23. $7(9 - 5)$

24. $5(3) - 2(4)$

25. $4 + 8 \div 2 + 6 \times 3$

26. $(7 + 8) \div (4 - 1)$

27. $5[2(8 + 5) - 15]$

28. $(6 + 8) \times (8 - 4)$

29. $12\left(\frac{6 + 30}{9 - 3}\right)$

30. $14 + 6 \times 2 - 8 \div 4$

31. $\frac{7(14) - 3(6)}{2}$

32. $14 \div [3(8 - 2) - 11]$

33. $3\left(\frac{9 + 13}{6}\right)$

34. $\frac{4(8 - 3)}{3 + 2}$

35. $3 + 4 \times 8 - 8 \div 4$

36. $13 + 4 \times 9$

37. $5(8 + 2) + 3(11 - 7)$

Evaluate each expression for $a = 2$ and $b = 6$.

38. $2(7a - b)$

39. $(a + b) \div a$

40. $3b \div (2a - 1) + b$

41. $\frac{5a + 2}{b}$

42. $\frac{3(b - 2)}{4(a + 1)}$

43. $9a + 4b \div 3$

Use the expression $r + 0.12m$ to calculate the cost of renting a car. The basic rate is r. The miles is driven is m. Determine the cost for the following.

44. The basic rate is $15.95. The car is driven 150 miles.

45. The basic rate is $32.50. The car is driven 257 miles.

Evaluate each expression for $s = 3$ and $t = 9$.

46. $8(4s - t)$

47. $(2t - 3s) \div 4$

48. $4t \div (6 + s)$

Use grouping symbols to make each equation true.

49. $6 + 8 \div 4 \times 2 = 7$

50. $4 \div 3 + 1 \times 2 = 2$

51. $5 + 4 \times 3 - 1 = 18$

Practice 1-4
• •
Example Exercises

Example 1

Find the value of each expression.

1. $|3.4|$

2. $|-6|$

3. $|-11.9|$

4. $|3|$

5. $\left|-\frac{2}{3}\right|$

6. $\left|-\frac{4}{9}\right|$

Find each sum.

7. $6 + (-4)$

8. $-2 + (-13)$

9. $-18 + 4$

10. $15 + (-32)$

11. $-27 + (-14)$

12 $8 + (-3)$

13. $|-13 + 6|$

14. $|14 + 13|$

15. $|-23 + (-19)|$

16. $-12.2 + 31.9$

17. $-47 + 47$

18. $-2.3 + (-13.9)$

19. $|-12| + |-21|$

20. $-17 + (-3) + 26$

21. $|14| + |-7|$

22. $19.8 + (-27.4)$

23. $5 + (-12) + 2$

24. $-9.4 + 6.8$

Example 2

Find each difference.

25. $13 - 6$

26. $19 - 35$

27. $-4 - 8$

28. $-14 - (-6)$

29. $18 - (-25)$

30. $-32 - 17$

31. $-6.8 - 14.6$

32. $-9.3 - (-23.9)$

33. $-8.2 - 0.8$

34. $|18 - 26.8|$

35. $|3.7 - (-6.8)|$

36. $|9.8| - |-15.7|$

37. $|-8 - (-32)|$

38. $|6 - 23|$

39. $|-4| - |13|$

40. $18.3 - (-8.1)$

41. $-3 - (-15)$

42. $6.4 - 17$

Example 3

Evaluate each expression for $c = -4$ and $d = -7$.

43. $|-c - d|$

44. $c - d$

45. $-c + d$

46. $|c + d|$

47. $|8 - c - d|$

48. $4 + c + d$

49. $-c - d - (-13)$

50. $c + d + 7$

51. $|25 - d + c|$

52. $|-c - 19 + d|$

53. $|c| - |-d|$

54. $|c - d| + |-17|$

• •

Practice 1-4

• •

Mixed Exercises

Simplify each expression.

1. $-12 + (-16)$ **2.** $5 + (-12)$ **3.** $5 + (-13)$

4. $\left| -32 - (-45) \right|$ **5.** $\left| -18 + 7 \right|$ **6.** $182 - (-240)$

7. $-6 - 9$ **8.** $-7 + (-26)$ **9.** $\left| 9 - 12 \right|$

10. $\left| -4 - 8 \right|$ **11.** $\left| -13 \right| + \left| 9 \right|$ **12.** $\left| -11 \right| - \left| -29 \right|$

Evaluate each expression.

13. $\left| b + 4 \right|$ for $b = -12$ **14.** $a - b$ for $a = 4$ and $b = 15$

15. $-x - y$ for $x = -2$ and $y = 5$ **16.** $\left| m - n \right|$ for $m = -6$ and $n = -13$

17. $-r - s$ for $r = -7$ and $s = -9$ **18.** $-u + v$ for $u = -2$ and $v = -12$

19. $\left| a - b \right|$ for $a = -7$ and $b = 14$ **20.** $\left| 13 - a + b \right|$ for $a = 7$ and $b = -15$

21. $6 - m + n$ for $m = 10$ and $n = -2$ **22.** $2 + x - y$ for $x = 5$ and $y = -3$

23. $\left| g \right| - \left| h \right|$ for $g = -11$ and $h = -29$ **24.** $-d + (-e) - 7$ for $d = 8$ and $e = -4$

Simplify each expression.

25. $-3 + (-6) + 14$ **26.** $-5 - 7$ **27.** $-4.2 - (-6.8)$

28. $\left| 14 \right| + \left| -19 \right|$ **29.** $-15 + (-29)$ **30.** $-6 + 2$

31. $2.83 - 3.82$ **32.** $4 + (-8) + 15$ **33.** $-6.3 + 8.2$

34. $\left| -4.8 - (-7.2) \right|$ **35.** $60 + (-125)$ **36.** $\left| -9 + 4 \right|$

37. $\left| 8 - 17 \right|$ **38.** $17 + (-13)$ **39.** $6 - 14 - (-20)$

40. $-2.62 + (-6.24)$ **41.** $\left| 4 + (-8) - 15 \right|$ **42.** $54 + (-72)$

43. $28 - (-16)$ **44.** $\left| -27 \right| - \left| 8 \right|$ **45.** $-13.9 - (-34.6)$

Evaluate each expression.

46. $3 - b + c$ for $b = -4$ and $c = -8$ **47.** $15 - m + n$ for $m = -2$ and $n = 40$

48. $\left| x + y \right|$ for $x = 12$ and $y = -7$ **49.** $a - b$ for $a = 15.8$ and $b = -27.4$

50. $r - s$ for $r = 120$ and $s = -150$ **51.** $\left| p - q + 5 \right|$ for $p = -2.5$ and $q = 3.8$

52. $-x + y$ for $x = 4$ and $y = -6$ **53.** $\left| s - t \right|$ for $s = 13$ and $t = 19$

54. $f - g$ for $f = -0.84$ and $g = -1.72$ **55.** $x + y$ for $x = 7$ and $y = -18$

56. $\left| k \right| - \left| -j \right|$ for $j = -2.76$ and $k = -9.28$ **57.** $\left| c + 5 \right| - \left| d \right|$ for $c = -9$ and $d = -11$

Practice 1-5

. . . .

Example Exercises

Example 1

Simplify each expression.

1. $-48 \div 6$

2. $(-23)(-3)$

3. $(-6)(32)$

4. $16 \div (-4)$

5. $(14)(-5)(-3)$

6. $(24)(-2) - 15$

7. $-13 + (-2)(17)$

8. $(-3)(4) + 8(-7)$

9. $(-7)(-3) - (-11)(-6)$

10. $\frac{-64}{8} + 3(-4)(2)$

11. $(-32) \div (-16) + 2(-6)$

12. $(-7)(-15) - \left(\frac{-18}{3}\right)$

Evaluate each expression for $x = -6, y = 3$, and $z = -5$.

13. $7x - z$

14. xyz

15. $4y \div (-3z)$

16. $\frac{10x}{y - 1}$

17. $\frac{xy}{z - 1}$

18. $5z - 4xy$

19. $\frac{2(x - y)}{5}$

20. $xy + 8z$

21. $\frac{-5(x + y)}{3}$

Example 2

Find the mean rounded to the nearest tenth.

22. $2, -7, 9, -7, -2, 8, 7$

23. $23, -10, -8, 33, 28, -13$

24. $-4, -7, 12, 10, -1, -7, 1, -9, 1, 12, -15$

25. $-25, -28, -6, 8, 2, -1, 9, -11, 3, 7$

26. $-1, 5, 0, 1, -4, -1, -8, 1, -4, 1, 0, -7, -19$

27. $-3, 8, 2, -11, 5, 0, 1, -5, -8, 1, 12, 17, 30$

Example 3

Simplify each expression.

28. $(-5)^3$

29. $(-4)^4$

30. -2^4

31. $4^2 + (-7)^2$

32. $-(-3)^3$

33. $-8^2 - (-9)^2$

34. $\left(\frac{-18}{6}\right)^3$

35. $-(-6)^3 \div (-3)^2$

36. $\frac{12^2}{(-2)^3}$

Evaluate each expression for $x = -4, y = -3$, and $z = 2$.

37. x^3

38. x^2z

39. y^5

40. $(x + z)^3$

41. $\frac{-6y^2}{z}$

42. $4x^2 - z$

43. $3x^2 \div y$

44. $3x - y^2$

45. x^2y^3

46. $\frac{6x}{-y} + z^3$

47. $x^3 \div z^2$

48. $(xyz)^2$

. . . .

Practice 1-5

• •

Mixed Exercises

Simplify each expression.

1. $(-2)(8)$ **2.** $(-6)(-9)$ **3.** $(-3)^4$

4. -2^5 **5.** $(6)(-8) + 30 \div (-6)$ **6.** $(-14)^2$

7. $2(-4)(-6)$ **8.** $(-4)(-5)$ **9.** $5(-6)$

10. $(-8)(5)(-3)$ **11.** -7^2 **12.** -3^5

13. $\frac{-68}{17}$ **14.** $\frac{(-4)(-13)}{-26}$ **15.** $\frac{225}{(-3)(-5)}$

Evaluate each expression.

16. x^3 for $x = -5$ **17.** $s^2t - 10$ for $s = -2$ and $t = 10$

18. $-2m + 4n^2$ for $m = -6$ and $n = -5$ **19.** $7v^2$ for $v = -7$

20. $-cd^2$ for $c = 2$ and $d = -4$ **21.** $(x + 4)^2$ for $x = -11$

22. $\left(\frac{a}{b}\right)^2 + b^3$ for $a = 24$ and $b = -6$ **23.** $4p^2 + 7q^3$ for $p = -3$ and $q = -2$

24. $(e + f)^4$ for $e = -3$ and $f = 7$ **25.** $5f^2 - z^2$ for $f = -1$ and $z = -4$

Simplify each expression.

26. $2^4 - 3^2 + 5^2$ **27.** $(-8)^2 - 4^3$ **28.** $32 \div (-7 + 5)^3$

29. $(-3)(14)$ **30.** $18 + 4^2 \div (-8)$ **31.** $26 \div (4 - (-9))$

32. $4^3 - (2 - 5)^3$ **33.** $-(-4)^3$ **34.** $(-8)(-5)(-3)$

35. $(-3)^2 - 4^2$ **36.** $3 \times (-15)$ **37.** $(-2)^6$

38. $(-6)(15)$ **39.** $\frac{-15}{(7 - 4)}$ **40.** $\frac{195}{-13}$

Evaluate each expression.

41. $(a + b)^2$ for $a = 6$ and $b = -8$ **42.** $d^3 \div e$ for $d = -6$ and $e = -3$

43. $(m + 5n)^3$ for $m = 2$ and $n = -1$ **44.** $j^5 - 5k$ for $j = -4$ and $k = -1$

45. $xy + z$ for $x = -4, y = 3$, and $z = -3$ **46.** $4s \div (-3t)$ for $s = -6$ and $t = -2$

47. $\frac{r^3}{s}$ for $r = -6$ and $s = -2$ **48.** $\frac{-h^5}{-4}$ for $h = 4$

Find the mean rounded to the nearest integer.

49. $5, 8, 2, -4, 7, -5$ **50.** $-15, 18, -13, 14, -17, -9, 1, -8$

51. $-30, -5, -18, 12, 6, 3, -19, 0, -3, 2$ **52.** $35, 27, -13, -19, 1, -3, 8, 15, -39$

53. $24, 7, 1, -9, -12, -32, 8, -11, 29, -11, -9$ **54.** $15, 19, -2, -7, -13, -21, 16, -22, 8, -9$

Practice 1-6
• •
Example Exercises

Example 1

Use a number line to compare the following.

1. $-\frac{11}{15}$ and $-\frac{4}{5}$ **2.** $\frac{3}{4}$ and $\frac{13}{16}$ **3.** $-\frac{7}{8}$ and $-\frac{4}{5}$ **4.** $-2\frac{3}{4}$ and -2.76

Example 2

Write in order from least to greatest.

5. $-\frac{3}{4}, -\frac{7}{8}, -\frac{2}{3}$ **6.** $-\frac{1}{3}, -0.3, -\frac{4}{11}$ **7.** $-\frac{5}{6}, \frac{1}{3}, -\frac{1}{2}$ **8.** $-2\frac{3}{4}, -2\frac{5}{8}, -2.7$

Example 3

Evaluate each expression for $f = \frac{3}{4}$ and $g = -\frac{2}{3}$.

9. fg **10.** $-\frac{9}{10}g$ **11.** $-2f$

12. $\frac{2}{3}f + \frac{3}{4}g$ **13.** $f - g - \frac{1}{2}$ **14.** $5f + g$

Evaluate each expression.

15. $5x - 7y$ for $x = -\frac{3}{4}$ and $y = -\frac{2}{3}$

16. $3m + 2n$ for $m = \frac{5}{6}$ and $n = -\frac{3}{8}$

17. $\frac{1}{2}a - \frac{2}{5}b$ for $a = \frac{2}{3}$ and $b = -\frac{5}{7}$

18. $5(a - b)$ for $a = -\frac{1}{2}$ and $b = -\frac{2}{3}$

Example 4

Evaluate each expression for $a = 20, b = 8,$ and $c = -25$.

19. $-\frac{5}{9}(c - 29)$ **20.** $-\frac{1}{2}(b + c)$ **21.** $\frac{3}{4}(a - b)$ **22.** $\frac{2}{3}(b - a)$

Use the expression $\frac{5}{9}$ (F − 32) to change the following from Fahrenheit to Celsius.

23. $14°F$ **24.** $68°F$ **25.** $-40°F$ **26.** $-13°F$

Example 5

Evaluate each expression.

27. $\frac{2a}{b}$ for $a = -\frac{2}{3}$ and $b = -\frac{1}{2}$ **28.** $\frac{x}{y}$ for $x = 4$ and $y = -\frac{4}{7}$

Practice 1-6

•••

Mixed Exercises

Use <, =, or > to compare.

1. -10.98 ■ -10.99

2. $-\frac{1}{3}$ ■ -0.3

3. $-\frac{1}{2}$ ■ $-\frac{5}{10}$

4. $-\frac{3}{8}$ ■ $-\frac{7}{16}$

Evaluate each expression.

5. xy for $x = \frac{3}{5}$ and $y = -\frac{3}{4}$

6. $\frac{m + n}{m}$ for $m = -\frac{3}{4}$ and $n = \frac{2}{3}$

7. $\frac{2a}{b}$ for $a = -\frac{3}{4}$ and $b = \frac{1}{2}$

8. $6xy$ for $x = -\frac{7}{3}$ and $y = -\frac{1}{6}$

9. $\frac{x}{y}$ for $x = -\frac{7}{8}$ and $y = 7$

10. xyz for $x = \frac{5}{6}, y = -\frac{3}{4}$, and $z = -\frac{1}{2}$

11. ab for $a = \frac{2}{3}$ and $b = -\frac{5}{6}$

12. $-12mn$ for $m = -\frac{7}{9}$ and $n = \frac{1}{8}$

Evaluate each expression for $a = 33$ and $b = -15$.

13. $\frac{3}{4}(b - 13)$

14. $-\frac{1}{4}(a - b)$

15. $\frac{2}{3}(a + b)$

16. $\frac{9}{4}(13 + b)$

17. $\frac{9}{5}(20 - b)$

18. $-\frac{5}{9}(-25 + a)$

Write in order from least to greatest.

19. $-\frac{8}{9}, -\frac{7}{8}, -\frac{22}{25}$

20. $-3\frac{4}{9}, -3.45, -3\frac{12}{25}$

21. $-\frac{1}{4}, -\frac{1}{5}, -\frac{1}{3}$

22. $-1.7, -1\frac{3}{4}, -1\frac{7}{9}$

Evaluate each expression for $x = -\frac{1}{2}$ and $y = -\frac{2}{3}$.

23. $x - y - \frac{1}{2}$

24. $\frac{2}{3}x + \frac{3}{4}y$

25. $4xy$

26. $\frac{1}{4}xy$

27. $\frac{x}{y}$

28. $-3x - 6y$

Evaluate each expression.

29. $\frac{4}{3}cd$ for $c = -\frac{1}{2}$ and $d = -\frac{2}{3}$

30. $-\frac{3}{7}(x - 52)$ for $x = 10$

31. $4x + 7y$ for $x = \frac{3}{4}$ and $y = -\frac{1}{3}$

32. $\frac{3a}{b}$ for $a = -\frac{5}{6}$ and $b = -\frac{3}{4}$

33. st for $s = -\frac{1}{4}$ and $t = -\frac{4}{5}$

34. mn for $m = -\frac{2}{5}$ and $n = -\frac{2}{3}$

Change the following from Fahrenheit to Celsius. Use $C = \frac{5}{9}(F - 32)$.

35. $-22°F$

36. $95°F$

37. $-31°F$

38. $50°F$

Practice 1-7

· ·

Example Exercises

Example 1

In a shipment of radios, 200 are selected at random. Four are found to be defective.

1. Find P(radio is defective).

2. Find P(radio is not defective).

3. Find the sum: P(radio is defective) $+ P$(radio is not defective).

4. There are 1500 radios in the shipment. Predict how many of the radios will not work.

5. A basketball player made 35 of 50 free throws. What is the probability that she will make the next one?

Some students conducted a taste test at lunch. The results are in the table below.

Type	Brand X	Brand Y	Brand Z
Number	18	15	17

6. What is the probability that the next student will prefer Brand X?

7. What is the probability that the next student will prefer Brand Z?

8. There are 400 students in that school. Predict the number that prefer Brand Y.

9. Will exactly 144 students prefer Brand X? Explain.

Example 2

Use the random number table to perform the following simulations.

10. A baseball player gets a hit 30% of the time.

   a. What is P(hits in each of the next two at bats)?

   b. What is P(no hits in the next two at bats)?

   c. What is P(at least one hit in the next two at bats)?

   d. What is P(exactly 1 hit in the next two at bats)?

11. There is a 60% chance of rain for each of the next three days.

   a. What is P(rain exactly one day)?

   b. What is P(rain exactly two days)?

   c. What is P(rain all three days)?

   d. What is P(it does not rain)?

Random Number Table			
23948	71477	12573	05954
65628	22310	09311	94684
41261	09943	34078	78481
34831	94510	21490	93312

· ·

Practice 1-7
••
Mixed Exercises

Use the random number table to perform the following simulations.

1. Suppose there are two stop lights on your way to school. Each one has a 20% chance of stopping you.

   a. Find P(stopped by both lights).

   b. Find P(stopped by no lights).

   c. Find P(stopped by exactly one light).

   d. Find P(stopped by at least one light).

Random Number Table			
23948	71477	12573	05954
65628	22310	09311	94684
41261	09943	34078	78481
34831	94510	21490	93312

2. Suppose there is a 50% chance of rain each of the next three days.

   a. Find P(will rain each of the next three days).

   b. Find P(will rain exactly one of the next three days).

   c. Find P(it will not rain the next three days).

A driver collected data on how long it takes her to drive to work.

Minutes	20	25	30
Times	4	8	2

3. Find P(the trip will take 25 minutes).

4. Find P(the trip will take 20 minutes).

5. Find P(the trip will take at least 25 minutes).

Use the data in the line plot to find each probability.

Student Birth Months

					X						X
X		X			X				X		X
X		X			X	X		X	X		X
X	X	X	X		X	X	X	X	X	X	X
JAN	FEB	MAR	APR	MAY	JUN	JUL	AUG	SEP	OCT	NOV	DEC

6. Find P(June).

7. Find P(October).

8. Find P(first six months of year).

9. Find P(May).

10. Find P(not December)

11. Find P(last three months of year).

A cereal manufacturer selects 100 boxes of cereal at random. Ninety-nine of the boxes are the correct weight.

12. Find P(the cereal box is the correct weight).

13. Find P(the cereal box is not the correct weight).

14. There are 24,000 boxes of cereal. Predict how many of the boxes are the correct weight.

Practice 1-8

• •

Example Exercises

Example 1

Find each sum.

1. $\begin{bmatrix} 3.9 \\ -5.2 \end{bmatrix} + \begin{bmatrix} -6.3 \\ -2.7 \end{bmatrix}$

2. $\begin{bmatrix} -0.5 & -5.3 \\ 8.1 & 1.5 \end{bmatrix} + \begin{bmatrix} -1.8 & 9.5 \\ -8.7 & 4.3 \end{bmatrix}$

3. $\begin{bmatrix} 0 & 0 \\ 0 & 0 \end{bmatrix} + \begin{bmatrix} -5 & 11 \\ 8 & -1 \end{bmatrix}$

4. $\begin{bmatrix} 1 & 0 & -5 \\ 2 & -3 & 0 \end{bmatrix} + \begin{bmatrix} -2 & 7 & 1 \\ -3 & 1 & 8 \end{bmatrix}$

5. $\begin{bmatrix} \frac{1}{2} & \frac{1}{4} \\ \frac{2}{3} & -\frac{1}{2} \end{bmatrix} + \begin{bmatrix} -\frac{1}{3} & \frac{1}{2} \\ -\frac{1}{6} & \frac{3}{4} \end{bmatrix}$

6. $\begin{bmatrix} -8 & 7 & 2 \end{bmatrix} + \begin{bmatrix} 4 & -8 & -4 \end{bmatrix}$

Find each difference.

7. $\begin{bmatrix} 0.7 & 1.8 \\ 2.1 & 0 \end{bmatrix} - \begin{bmatrix} -1.9 & 2.4 \\ -3 & 0.9 \end{bmatrix}$

8. $\begin{bmatrix} 1 & 3 \\ -4 & 8 \end{bmatrix} - \begin{bmatrix} 2 & -8 \\ -1 & 2 \end{bmatrix}$

9. $\begin{bmatrix} -\frac{4}{5} & \frac{3}{4} \end{bmatrix} - \begin{bmatrix} \frac{4}{5} & -\frac{1}{6} \end{bmatrix}$

10. $\begin{bmatrix} 1 & -5 & 7 \\ 2 & -3 & 6 \end{bmatrix} - \begin{bmatrix} 5 & 2 & -1 \\ 0 & 2 & -3 \end{bmatrix}$

11. $\begin{bmatrix} 3.9 \\ -7.1 \end{bmatrix} - \begin{bmatrix} -4.2 \\ 10.8 \end{bmatrix}$

12. $\begin{bmatrix} -\frac{1}{2} & -\frac{7}{4} \\ \frac{1}{3} & \frac{1}{2} \end{bmatrix} - \begin{bmatrix} -\frac{3}{4} & \frac{2}{3} \\ -\frac{5}{6} & -\frac{3}{7} \end{bmatrix}$

Example 2

13. Use the tables below to find the total number of tickets sold in each category for each type of performance. Write your answer as a table.

Saturday Number of Tickets

Performance	Adult	Child	Senior
Matinee	22	23	15
Evening	51	23	18

Sunday Number of Tickets

Performance	Adult	Child	Senior
Matinee	28	17	9
Evening	49	27	18

14. Use the tables below to find the total number of medals of each type won by each country. Write your answer as a table.

1994 Winter Olympic Games

Country	Gold	Silver	Bronze
Kenya	0	0	0
Japan	1	2	2
United States	6	5	2

Source: *The World Almanac 1995*

1992 Summer Olympic Games

Country	Gold	Silver	Bronze
Kenya	2	4	2
Japan	3	8	11
United States	37	34	37

Source: *The World Almanac 1995*

Practice 1-8

Mixed Exercises

Add each pair of matrices. Then subtract the second matrix from the first matrix in each pair.

1. $\begin{bmatrix} -2 & 3 \\ -4 & -8 \end{bmatrix}, \begin{bmatrix} 5 & 6 \\ -10 & -6 \end{bmatrix}$
2. $\begin{bmatrix} 1 & -2 & 3 \\ 4 & -8 & 0 \end{bmatrix}, \begin{bmatrix} -1 & 5 & -9 \\ 4 & -5 & 1 \end{bmatrix}$
3. $\begin{bmatrix} -\frac{4}{5} & \frac{2}{3} \end{bmatrix}, \begin{bmatrix} -\frac{1}{3} & \frac{1}{4} \end{bmatrix}$

Find the increase in population for each state. Write your answer in a table.

4.

1950 Population
(rounded to the nearest hundred thousand)

State	Population
Arkansas	1,900,000
Indiana	3,900,000
Michigan	6,400,000

1990 Population
(rounded to the nearest hundred thousand)

State	Population
Arkansas	2,400,000
Indiana	5,500,000
Michigan	9,300,000

Source: Bureau of the Census, U.S. Dept. of Commerce

Find each sum or difference.

5. $\begin{bmatrix} \frac{2}{3} & -6 \end{bmatrix} + \begin{bmatrix} -\frac{3}{4} & 10 \end{bmatrix}$
6. $\begin{bmatrix} -3 & 2.5 & -6 \\ 10 & 3 & -4 \end{bmatrix} - \begin{bmatrix} 6 & -8 & 2 \\ 0 & -2 & 6 \end{bmatrix}$
7. $\begin{bmatrix} \frac{7}{8} & -\frac{1}{2} \\ \frac{3}{5} & -\frac{1}{3} \end{bmatrix} + \begin{bmatrix} -\frac{1}{2} & \frac{4}{3} \\ -\frac{3}{4} & \frac{3}{2} \end{bmatrix}$

8. $\begin{bmatrix} -6 & 2 & -8 \\ 2 & 5 & -9 \\ 11 & 12 & -7 \end{bmatrix} - \begin{bmatrix} 4 & -8 & 11 \\ 5 & -6 & -8 \\ 1 & 15 & -8 \end{bmatrix}$
9. $\begin{bmatrix} 2.8 & -3.7 & 9.4 \\ 0.5 & -5.2 & 0.9 \\ 3.7 & -1.9 & 2.2 \end{bmatrix} - \begin{bmatrix} 1.7 & -0.8 & 6.1 \\ 1.9 & 5.7 & -3.3 \\ 2.9 & -1.9 & -2.2 \end{bmatrix}$

10. Determine the change in the number of votes for each party from 1988 to 1992. Write your answer in the form of a matrix.

1988 Presidential Election

State	Democrat	Republican
Alabama	549,506	815,576
Colorado	621,453	728,177
Iowa	670,557	545,355
Minnesota	1,109,471	962,337

1992 Presidential Election

State	Democrat	Republican
Alabama	690,080	804,283
Colorado	629,681	562,850
Iowa	586,353	504,891
Minnesota	1,020,997	747,841

Source: Voter News Service; Federal Election Commission

Practice 1-9

• •

Example Exercises

Example 1

Use the spreadsheet at right for Exercises 1–3.

1. Write the spreadsheet formulas for cells B2, C2, and D2.

2. Find the values for cells B2, C2, and D2.

3. Find the values for cells B3, C3, and D3.

	A	B	C	D
1	x	$x/2$	$x \wedge 2$	$4x$
2	2	■	■	■
3	−4	■	■	■

Use the spreadsheet at right for Exercises 4–6.

4. Write the spreadsheet formulas for cells B2, C2, D2.

5. Find the values for cells B2, C2, and D2.

6. Find the values for cells B3, C3, and D3.

	A	B	C	D
1	a	$3a$	$(a+2)/3$	$a\wedge3 + 2$
2	7	■	■	■
3	4	■	■	■

Example 2

Evaluate each spreadsheet expression.

7. Area of a triangle: $0.5 * A2 * B2$

   a. for A2 = 6 and B2 = 4

   b. for A2 = 12.7 and B2 = 4.8

8. Area of a square: $A2\wedge2$

   a. for A2 = 5.4

   b. for A2 = 11.7

9. Cost of item plus tax: $A2 + A2 * B2$

   a. for A2 = $7.95 and B2 = 0.06

   b. for A2 = $15.95 and B2 = 0.08

10. Mean of three numbers: $(A2 + B2 + C2)/3$

    a. for A2 = 88, B2 = 93, and C2 = 89

    b. for A2 = 5.8, B2 = 19.2, and C2 = 15.8

Use the spreadsheet at right for Exercises 11–12.

11. A company uses a spreadsheet to calculate payroll. Determine the amount of pay for each employee.

12. Write the spreadsheet formula to calculate total pay.

	A	B	C	D
1	Name	Hours	Rate	Pay
2	Raul	38	$6.25	■
3	Nhan	39.5	$7.50	■
4	Sue	37	$6.75	■
5			Totals	■

• •

Practice 1-9
• •
Mixed Exercises

1. Evaluate the spreadsheet expression (A3 + B3)/C3.

    a. for A3 = 6.8, B3 = 7.2, and C3 = 4

    b. for A3 = –12, B3 = 35 and C3 = –2

Use the spreadsheet at right for Exercises 2–4.

2. Write the spreadsheet formulas for cells B2 and C2.

3. Find the value for cells B2 and C2.

4. Find the value for cells B3 and C3.

	A	B	C
1	x	$x \wedge 3$	$(x + 4) / 5$
2	5	■	■
3	–1	■	■

5. Evaluate the spreadsheet expression (B2 + C2)^2.

    a. for B2 = 8 and C2 = 14

    b. for B2 = –12.6 and C2 = 8.6

    c. for B2 = –7 and C2 = 3

6. A teacher wishes to use these percents to compute grades.

    Homework   20%
    Quiz   35%
    Test   45%

    Use the spreadsheet at right to answer **a–b.**

    a. Write the formula for cell E2.

    b. Find the values for cells E2 and E3.

	A	B	C	D	E
1	Student	Homework	Quiz	Test	Grade
2	A. Garcia	90	96	94	■
3	C. Ho	94	92	88	■

7. Evaluate the spreadsheet expression 0.5 * B2 * (C2 + D2).

    a. for B2 = 10, C2 = 4, and D2 = 8

    b. for B2 = 4, C2 = –4, and D2 = –6

8. Evaluate the spreadsheet expression (A2 + 2 * B2)/4.

    a. for A2 = 2 and B2 = 8

    b. for A2 = 1.6 and B2 = –2.5

Use the spreadsheet at right for Exercises 9–11.

9. Write the spreadsheet formulas for cells B2, C2, D2.

10. Find the values for cells B2, C2, and D2.

11. Find the values for cells B3, C3, and D3.

	A	B	C	D
1	x	$x / 4$	$(2x) \wedge 2$	$x^2 + x$
2	2	■	■	■
3	6	■	■	■

Chapter Project Manager
• •
Chapter 1 The Big Dig

Getting Started Read about the project on page 3 of your textbook. As you work on the project, you will need a tape measure or ruler, and materials to make accurate and attractive graphs. Keep all of your work for the project in a folder, along with this Project Manager Checklist.

Checklist and Suggestions

❑ Measure your radius bone and the radius bone of every student in your class. (p. 9)

Measure from the base of your thumb to the bend in your arm. Separate your data according to sex.

❑ Display the data in a graph. (p. 9)

Choose the best type of graph for displaying the data.

❑ Find the mean, median, and mode. (p. 9)

See pp. 4 and 5 for help. Be sure to show your work.

❑ Measure your tibia, humerus, and radius bone lengths to calculate your height. (p. 29)

Use the correct formula for calculating your height. Try all three formulas to find the most accurate one.

❑ Choose one radius measurement you took and calculate that person's height. (p. 29)

Be careful to use the correct formula for a male or a female.

❑ Organize the data by male and female. Look for any differences between the sexes. (p. 39)

Choose an effective table or graph.

❑ Collect data from several adults. (p. 49)

Use family members, teachers, or neighbors.

❑ Use a spreadsheet to organize data. Compare predicted heights with measured heights. (p. 49)

Plan first! You may need many columns.

Scoring Rubric

3 You choose appropriate types of graphs and charts. You label graphs correctly and completely and devise accurate scales. Your formulas and calculations are accurate. You make an easy-to-follow spreadsheet. You reason correctly and clearly express all explanations.

2 You correctly choose a spreadsheet and the correct graphs and formulas. You have minor errors in scale or computation. Your reasoning and explanations are essentially correct, but you write some awkward or unclear passages.

1 You make graphs and select formulas that are somewhat correct. Your calculations are somewhat correct and need improvement. You provide adequate explanations.

0 You leave out or do not complete major elements of the project.

Your Evaluation of Project Evaluate your work, based on the *Scoring Rubric*.

Teacher's Evaluation of Project

• •

✔ Checkpoint 1

• •

For use after 1-5

Simplify.

1. $12 - 3(2)$ **2.** $(-5)^2 - 3^2$ **3.** $\dfrac{20 - 4 \cdot 3}{5 + 3}$ **4.** $[2(6 - 3) + 8] - 2^3$

Evaluate each expression for $s = -5$ and $t = 3$.

5. $-s$ **6.** $3t^2 + s$ **7.** $\left|3t + 5s\right|$ **8.** $t - 12$ **9.** $\left|-4t\right| - \left|3s\right|$

10. Writing Is $(-3)^2$ positive or negative? Explain.

11. The mean of a set of test scores was 82 and the median was 84. Which is the correct set of test scores?

     A. 94, 75, 84, 87, 82, 79, 85   **B.** 85, 81, 91, 83, 75, 84, 88

     C. 78, 83, 70, 90, 89, 80, 84   **D.** 85, 79, 87, 86, 84, 71, 82

12. Write an equation to describe the relationship shown in the table.

Bags	Oranges
1	12
5	60
9	108

13. Suppose tickets to a ball game cost $3.50 each. Write an equation to find how much it would cost to buy n number of tickets.

- - - ✂ -

✔ Checkpoint 2

• •

For use after 1-8

Evaluate each expression.

1. $3x - 2y$ for $x = \frac{7}{9}, y = \frac{5}{6}$ **2.** $4a - 6b$ for $a = -7$ and $b = 1\frac{1}{2}$ **3.** $\frac{m}{n}$ for $m = -\frac{3}{4}, n = \frac{5}{8}$

Simplify.

4. $\begin{bmatrix} 1 & -2 & 0 \\ 3 & -1 & 5 \\ 1 & 3 & -6 \end{bmatrix} + \begin{bmatrix} 3 & -2 & 5 \\ 7 & -2 & -3 \\ 1 & -8 & 2 \end{bmatrix}$ **5.** $\begin{bmatrix} 3.5 & -2.8 \\ 1.7 & 3.0 \end{bmatrix} - \begin{bmatrix} 1.7 & 8.2 \\ -9.1 & 3.9 \end{bmatrix}$

6. Open-ended Write three negative fractions in order from smallest to largest.

Use the spreadsheet for Exercises 7-9.

7. Write the formulas for cells B2, C2, and D2.

8. Find the values for cells B2, C2, and D2.

9. Find the values for cells B3, C3, and D3.

	A	B	C	D
1	n	$4n$	$n \wedge 3$	$n / 2$
2	-2	■	■	■
3	4	■	■	■

Chapter Assessment

Form A

Chapter 1

Find the mean, median, and mode of each set of data. Round to the nearest tenth.

1. $6, -4, 3, 2, -2, 1, 6$

2. $91, 92, 93, 88, 86, 92$

3. Draw a graph of the table.

Crude Oil Overview (in quadrillion Btu)

	1960	1970	1980	1990
Production	14.93	20.40	18.25	15.57
Import	2.20	2.81	11.19	12.77
Export	0.43	0.55	1.16	1.82

Source: U.S. Department of Energy

4. Explain why you chose this type of graph.

5. Why did you use this scale for your graph?

Use an equation to model the relationship in each table.

6.

Months	Saved
1	$150
2	$300
3	$450
4	$600

7.

Traveled	Remaining
10 mi	90 mi
25 mi	75 mi
40 mi	60 mi
88 mi	12 mi

8. Using the equation from Exercise 6, calculate the amount saved in seven months.

9. The mean on a set of test scores was 88 and the median was 86. Which is the correct set of test scores?

A. 94, 86, 86, 87, 82, 79, 88

B. 85, 88, 95, 83, 82, 86, 97

C. 88, 86, 81, 97, 90, 91, 83

D. 85, 89, 97, 86, 85, 81, 84

Simplify.

10. $4 + 8 \div 2 + 6 \times 2$

11. $12 - (-3)$

12. $-6(-3) + -2$

13. $(-8)^2 \div -2$

Evaluate each expression.

14. $5x + 4$ for $x = 5$

15. $y^2 \div z$ for $y = -12$ and $z = -9$

16. $|6 - 2m|$ for $m = 7$

17. $-2(2s - 3t)$ for $s = -5.2$ and $t = 1.9$

18. $\frac{a}{b}$ for $a = \frac{2}{3}$ and $b = -\frac{5}{6}$

19. $\frac{2d - 3}{-5}$ for $d = 9$

Chapter Assessment (continued)   Form A

Chapter 1

Compare each pair of numbers using the symbol for *greater than*.

20. $-2\frac{3}{4}, -2\frac{7}{8}$

21. $\frac{2}{9}, 0.23$

22. Critical Thinking Explain what the error is in the work shown below.

$$9 + 12 \div 3 = 21 \div 3$$
$$= 7$$

Find the sum or difference.

23. $\begin{bmatrix} -2 & 13 \\ 8 & -6 \end{bmatrix} + \begin{bmatrix} 8 & -17 \\ -8 & -4 \end{bmatrix}$

24. $\begin{bmatrix} 1.2 & -6.8 \\ 0.4 & 0 \\ 2.3 & -8 \end{bmatrix} - \begin{bmatrix} 2.5 & 3.6 \\ -2.7 & -0.1 \\ 2.4 & -7.3 \end{bmatrix}$

The formula for the perimeter of a rectangle is $P = 2(l + w)$. The spreadsheet gives the dimensions, in feet, for three rectangles.

	A	B	C
1	Length	Width	Perimeter
2	20	23	■
3	12.5	17.6	■
4	35.2	18.7	■

25. Write a formula for cell C2 to find the perimeter of the rectangle in row 2.

26. Find the perimeter of each rectangle.

You have a coin bank containing dimes, nickels, and quarters. You grab a handful and find that you have four dimes, seven nickels, and three quarters. Find the probability that each is the next coin you select.

27. P(quarter).

28. P(coin worth more than a nickel).

29. If the bank contains 126 coins, how may dimes would you expect to have?

30. Open-ended. Write an expression, containing three integers, that has a value of zero. One integer should be inside absolute value symbols.

Chapter Assessment

Form B

Chapter 1

Find the mean, median, and mode of each set of data. Round to the nearest tenth.

1. $10, 9, 8, -2, 7, 8, 9, -9$

2. $9.8, 9.7, 9.2, 9.8, 9.5$

3. Use the table below to draw a graph.

High School Graduates (in thousands)

	1990	1991	1992	1993
Male	1169	1139	1216	1118
Female	1185	1137	1182	1219

Source: American College Testing Program;
Bureau of the Census; U.S. Dept. of Labor

4. Explain your choice of graph type and scale.

Use an equation to model the relationship in each table.

5.

Number	Cost
1	$3.45
2	$6.90
3	$10.35
4	$13.80

6.

Games Played	Games Remaining
10	152
50	112
100	62
162	0

7. Using the equation from Exercise 5, find the cost of 15 items.

8. Which of the following expressions has a value of 30?

   I. $6 \times 4 - 8 \div 2 + 2$
  II. $6 + 4 \times (3 + 10) \div 2$
 III. $5 + 4 \times 5 + 10 \div 2$

  A. I and II   **B.** II and III   **C.** I and III   **D.** none of the above

Simplify.

9. $-3 + 8 \div 2 + 7$

10. $-23.8 + 19.4$

11. $-7(2) - (-12)$

12. $-63 \div 9$

Evaluate each expression.

13. $3x - 9$ for $x = 3$

14. $y^2 \div z$ for $y = -14$ and $z = 4$

15. $|m| - |-2n|$ for $m = -11$ and $n = 8$

16. $-2(s - 6t)$ for $s = 2.9$ and $t = -3.8$

17. $\frac{a}{b}$ for $a = -\frac{3}{4}$ and $b = \frac{7}{8}$

18. $\frac{4 + 2d}{-2}$ for $d = -7$

Chapter Assessment (continued)   Form B

Chapter 1

Use <, =, > to compare.

19. -8.98 ■ -8.94

20. $2\frac{5}{11}$ ■ 2.45

21. Writing Explain why the equation below is not always true.

$$|x| = x$$

Find the sum or difference.

22. $\begin{bmatrix} -2 & 13 \\ 8 & -6 \end{bmatrix} - \begin{bmatrix} 8 & -17 \\ -8 & -4 \end{bmatrix}$

23. $\begin{bmatrix} 1.2 & -6.8 \\ 0.4 & 0 \\ 2.3 & -8 \end{bmatrix} + \begin{bmatrix} 2.5 & 3.6 \\ -2.7 & -0.1 \\ 2.4 & -7.3 \end{bmatrix}$

The formula for the area of a circle is $A = 3.14r^2$. The spreadsheet gives the radius in feet for three circles.

	A	B
1	Radius	Area
2	3	■
3	1.5	■
4	8.2	■

24. Write a formula for cell B2 to find the area of the circle in row 2.

25. Find the area of each circle. Round to the nearest tenth.

You select colored golf balls at random from a box and record the color. Use the data in the line plot to find the probability that each is the next color selected.

				X
		X		X
X		X		X
X	X	X		X
X	X	X	X	X
BLACK	**RED**	**BLUE**	**YELLOW**	**GREEN**

26. $P(\text{red})$

27. $P(\text{blue or green})$

28. $P(\text{not black})$

29. Open-ended Choose five different integers so that the mean will be 11 and the median will be 10.

Alternative Assessment
· ·
Chapter 1

Give complete answers. Show all your work.

TASK 1

A teacher gives a test to a class of 25 students. The grades are as follows:

40% of students receive a grade of C (test scores of 70−79%),

40% of students receive a grade of either B (80−89%) or D (60−69%),

20% of students receive a grade of either A (90−100%) or F (0−59%).

  a. Invent 25 test scores, based on the information above.

  b. From your data, determine the mean, median, and mode for the class.

  c. Select and draw the best type of graph to display your data.

  d. What is the probability that a student, picked at random, received an A?

TASK 2

Two students write the following expressions to answer an exercise:

$$7 + 4(5 - 3)^2 + \frac{9}{3} \quad \text{and} \quad \frac{9}{3} + (5 - 3)^2 \cdot 4 + 7.$$

  a. Simplify the two expressions. List each step you use.

  b. Explain the similarities in the steps.

  c. Make up another expression that uses the same numbers and operations but has a different answer. Then simplify, listing each step.

Alternative Assessment (continued)

Chapter 1

TASK 3

a. A friend asks you for help with adding, subtracting, multiplying, and dividing positive and negative integers. Using your own words, make up rules for each operation: addition, subtraction, multiplication, and division. Make up two examples that demonstrate how each rule works.

b. The same friend is having trouble comparing rational numbers. Write an explanation that will tell your friend how to decide if a rational number is greater than, less than, or equal to, another rational number.

c. Add the two matrices below. Then subtract the second matrix from the first.

$$\begin{bmatrix} -2 & 5.1 \\ 1.4 & -3 \end{bmatrix}, \begin{bmatrix} 4 & -6.1 \\ 0 & -3.2 \end{bmatrix}$$

TASK 4

You plan to buy a car that costs $12,000. You have saved $2,000 to use any way you want towards the purchase. Two different banks have agreed to give you a loan for the car at the following terms:

Bank A offers you: $12,000 loan, 9% interest rate, for five years.

Bank B offers you: $10,000 loan, 8% interest rate, for four years.

a. Create a spreadsheet to compare the two loans. Explain which loan you will choose. You may use the equation $I = prt$, where I is the total interest paid, p is the amount borrowed, r is the interest rate, and t is the number of years.

b. Write an equation for the cost of several cars whose price is the same as the one that you plan to buy. Explain what the variables in your equation represent.

Cumulative Review

•••

Chapter 1

For Exercises 1–4, choose the correct letter.

1. Which set of data has a mean of 19 and a median of 17?

   A. 25, 13, 16, 22, 18   **B.** 12, 19, 20, 13, 21

   C. 17, 16, 25, 27, 15   **D.** 23, 14, 15, 26, 17

2. Simplify the expression $8 \times 4 + 6 \div 2 + 8$.

   A. 27   **B.** 43   **C.** 8   **D.** 48

3. Which matrix is the sum of $\begin{bmatrix} -3 & 5 \\ -8 & 7 \end{bmatrix} + \begin{bmatrix} 3 & -8 \\ 9 & -2 \end{bmatrix}$?

   A. $\begin{bmatrix} 0 & -3 \\ 1 & 5 \end{bmatrix}$ **B.** $\begin{bmatrix} 0 & -13 \\ 1 & 5 \end{bmatrix}$ **C.** $\begin{bmatrix} 0 & 3 \\ 1 & -9 \end{bmatrix}$ **D.** $\begin{bmatrix} -6 & -3 \\ -1 & 5 \end{bmatrix}$

4. Which of the following expressions has a value of 12?

   I. $8 + 4 \times 4 \div 2 + 2$
   II. $(8 + 4) \times [4 \div (2 + 2)]$
   III. $(8 + 4 \times 4) \div (2 + 2)$

   A. I only   **B.** II only   **C.** I and III   **D.** II and III

Draw a multiple bar graph for the table.

5.
National Income by Industry
(billions of dollars)

Industry	1970	1980	1990
Construction	47.4	126.6	234.4
Transportation	31.5	85.8	139.4
Retail	79.9	189.4	392.1

Source: Bureau of Economic Analysis

Evaluate each expression.

6. $3x + 5$ for $x = 3$

7. $4x^3$ for $x = -2$

8. $2(a + 3)$ for $a = -7$

9. $-3mn$ for $m = -4$ and $n = 2$

10. $|p| - |3q|$ for $p = -12.3$ and $q = -6.1$

11. gh for $g = \frac{3}{4}$ and $h = -\frac{2}{9}$

12. $|3d + 4|$ for $d = -9$

13. $3(s + 2t)$ for $s = 2.7$ and $t = -3.9$

14. $\frac{a}{b}$ for $a = \frac{2}{3}$ and $b = -\frac{5}{6}$

15. $\frac{3x}{-2}$ for $x = 4$

Cumulative Review (continued)

Chapter 1

Compare each pair of numbers using the symbol for *less than*.

16. $\frac{2}{9}, \frac{1}{5}$

17. $-\frac{7}{8}, -\frac{13}{16}$

18. $3\frac{2}{3}, 3.6$

19. $-5.27, -5\frac{7}{25}$

Find the sum or difference.

20. $\begin{bmatrix} 6.7 & -2.6 \\ 3.5 & -1.7 \end{bmatrix} + \begin{bmatrix} -3.3 & 2.9 \\ -0.2 & 1.1 \end{bmatrix}$

21. $\begin{bmatrix} 3.9 & -3.5 \\ 0.8 & 1.7 \end{bmatrix} - \begin{bmatrix} -2.3 & 6.5 \\ 2.9 & -2.6 \end{bmatrix}$

22. $\begin{bmatrix} 6 & 5 \\ -7 & 1 \\ -3 & 8 \end{bmatrix} - \begin{bmatrix} -5 & 2 \\ -8 & 1 \\ 4 & -6 \end{bmatrix}$

23. $\begin{bmatrix} -7 & 8 & 2 \\ 3 & 9 & -2 \end{bmatrix} + \begin{bmatrix} 5 & 9 & -3 \\ 1 & -7 & 9 \end{bmatrix}$

Use an equation to model the relationship in each table.

24.

Items	Cost
1	$1.50
2	$3.00
3	$4.50

25.

Worked	Remaining
1.5 h	6.5 h
3 h	5 h
4.5 h	3.5 h

26. In a shipment of memory chips, 200 are selected at random. Two are found to be defective.

  a. What is P(memory chip is defective)?

  b. What is P(memory chip is not defective)?

  c. There are 2400 memory chips in the shipment. Predict how many of the memory chips will be defective.

  d. **Writing** Explain why the answer for (**c**) may not be the actual number of defective memory chips.

Use the following spreadsheet for Exercises 27 and 28.

	A	B	C	D
1	Name	Hours	Rate	Pay
2	Adam	28.5	$6.50	■
3	Jose	29.5	$6.25	■
4	Franz	32.0	$7.00	■

27. Write the formula for cell D2.

28. Calculate the pay for Adam, Jose, and Franz.

29. **Open-ended** Write five different numbers that together have a mean of 10 and a median of 10.

Standardized Test Practice
Chapter 1

For Exercises 1–14, choose the correct letter.

1. The mode of a set of ten numbers is 4. The median is 9. Which of the following *cannot* be the mean?

   A. 4   **B.** 9

   C. 12   **D.** 13

   E. 20

2. Compare the quantities in Column A and Column B.

Column A	**Column B**
the reciprocal of 2	the opposite of 2

   A. The quantity in Column A is greater.

   B. The quantity in Column B is greater.

   C. The two quantities are equal.

   D. The relationship cannot be determined on the basis of the information supplied.

3. The total cost for bus tickets for a family equals the number of adults at $1.00 each plus the number of children at $.50 each. Which equation could be used to model this?

   A. $T = 1a + 0.5c$ **B.** $c = 1a + 0.5c$

   C. $T = c(a + 0.5)$ **D.** $c = a(1 + 0.5c)$

   E. $T = 1.5a + c$

4. To simplify $15 + 5(12 \div 4) \cdot 2$, you should first calculate which of the following?

   A. $15 + 5$ **B.** $12 \div 4$

   C. $5 \cdot 12$ **D.** $5 \div 4$

   E. $4 \cdot 2$

5. Compare the quantities in Column A and Column B.

Column A	**Column B**
$3 - \left(\frac{2}{3} \cdot 6\right)$	$\left(3 - \frac{2}{3}\right) \cdot 6$

   A. The quantity in Column A is greater.

   B. The quantity in Column B is greater.

   C. The two quantities are equal.

   D. The relationship cannot be determined on the basis of the information supplied.

6. Evaluate $2(b^2 - 4b) + 3$ for $b = 4$.

   A. 0   **B.** 2

   C. 8   **D.** -16

   E. none of the above

7. The opposite of -12 is which of the following?

   A. -21 **B.** 12

   C. $\frac{1}{12}$ **D.** $-\frac{1}{12}$

   E. none of the above

8. Simplify $(-4)^3$.

   A. -12 **B.** 12

   C. -64 **D.** 64

   E. none of the above

9. Which of the following is equivalent to $x \div y$?

   A. $\frac{1}{x} - y$ **B.** $x \cdot \frac{1}{y}$

   C. $\frac{y}{x}$ **D.** $x - \frac{1}{y}$

   E. none of the above

10. Which of the following is true?

    A. $\frac{1}{4} < \frac{1}{3}$ **B.** $-\frac{1}{2} > -\frac{1}{4}$

    C. $-\frac{1}{4} > \frac{1}{3}$ **D.** $\frac{1}{2} < -\frac{1}{3}$

    E. none of the above

11. Compare the quantities in Column A and Column B for the matrix $\begin{bmatrix} 1 & -2 \\ 2 & -1 \end{bmatrix}$.

Column A	**Column B**
row 1 column 2	row 2 column 1

    A. The quantity in Column I is greater.

    B. The quantity in Column II is greater.

    C. The two quantities are equal.

    D. The relationship cannot be determined on the basis of the information supplied.

Standardized Test Practice (continued)

Chapter 1

12. Simplify $|17.3 - 22.7|$.

    A. 5.4   **B.** 15.4

    C. −5.4   **D.** −15.4

    E. none of the above

13. Which of the following is an irrational number?

    A. $\sqrt{2}$ **B.** 0.125

    C. $\frac{1}{3}$ **D.** 101

    E. none of the above

14. Twenty students participate in a taste test. Four students prefer salad dressing X, seven students prefer dressing Y, and the remaining prefer dressing Z. Compare the quantities in Column A and Column B.

Column A	Column B
probability that a student prefers dressing Z	probability that a student does not prefer dressing Y

    A. The quantity in Column A is greater.

    B. The quantity in Column B is greater.

    C. The two quantities are equal.

    D. The relationship cannot be determined on the basis of the information supplied.

For Exercises 15–19, write your answer.

15. Draw a line plot for this set of data: 21, 22, 26, 22, 21, 27, 23, 22, 21, 22, 26, 23. Find the mean, median, and mode.

16. Evaluate $6a + 12 \div 3a$ for $a = 2$.

17. Write the spreadsheet formula you would use to calculate the mean of the three numbers in column A. Write the result that would be in cell A4.

	A
1	16.2
2	17.4
3	15.1
4	■

18. **Open-ended** Create two 2×2 matrices, explain how to add them, and show the addition.

19. Simplify $\begin{bmatrix} 1 & -1 \\ 0 & 4 \end{bmatrix} - \begin{bmatrix} 2 & 1 \\ 1 & -1 \end{bmatrix}$.

For Exercises 20–22, mark your answers in the free response grid.

20. Evaluate $\frac{d^3}{d + 4}$ for $d = 4$.

21. Simplify $-17 - (-26)$.

22. Evaluate $\frac{-a}{3} + 2ab$ for $a = -6$ and $b = 4$.

Chapter 1

Bubble Grid Answer Sheet for Standardized Test Practice

1. Ⓐ Ⓑ Ⓒ Ⓓ Ⓔ
2. Ⓐ Ⓑ Ⓒ Ⓓ Ⓔ
3. Ⓐ Ⓑ Ⓒ Ⓓ Ⓔ
4. Ⓐ Ⓑ Ⓒ Ⓓ Ⓔ
5. Ⓐ Ⓑ Ⓒ Ⓓ Ⓔ
6. Ⓐ Ⓑ Ⓒ Ⓓ Ⓔ
7. Ⓐ Ⓑ Ⓒ Ⓓ Ⓔ
8. Ⓐ Ⓑ Ⓒ Ⓓ Ⓔ
9. Ⓐ Ⓑ Ⓒ Ⓓ Ⓔ
10. Ⓐ Ⓑ Ⓒ Ⓓ Ⓔ
11. Ⓐ Ⓑ Ⓒ Ⓓ Ⓔ
12. Ⓐ Ⓑ Ⓒ Ⓓ Ⓔ
13. Ⓐ Ⓑ Ⓒ Ⓓ Ⓔ
14. Ⓐ Ⓑ Ⓒ Ⓓ Ⓔ
15.

16.

17.

18.

19.

20.

21.

22.

Chapter 1 Answers

Alternative Activity 1-1

1. More cans are manufactured than are recycled.

2.

Manufactured (in billions)		Recycled (in billions)	
1989	45.7	1989	27.8
1990	49.2	1990	31.3
1991	53.0	1991	33.0
1992	54.9	1992	37.3
1993	58.0	1993	36.6

3. 1989 to 1993 **4.** 0 to 60 **5.** Both lines are rising; they do not intersect. **6.** All cans that were manufactured would have to be recycled.

Alternative Activity 1-4

1. 1 yd **2.** to the right **3.** 5 yd to the left of S
4. $5 - 9 = -4$ **5a.** -4 **5b.** -4
6a. 10 **6b.** 10 **7a.** -7 **7b.** -7
8. the opposite of the number

Alternative Activity 1-7

1–3. Answers may vary.

Reteaching 1-1

1. a line graph to show data changing over time **2.** from 0 to 16,000 with every 2000 employees labeled **3.** from 1940 to 1975 with every 5 yr labeled on the axis

4.

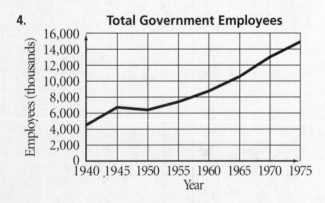

Total Government Employees

5. The number of government employees has generally increased from 1940 to 1975 except for the time from 1945 to 1950.

Reteaching 1-2

Answers may vary. Sample:
1. $4q = g$ **2.** $t = 6p$ **3.** $m = 2 + p$ **4.** $j = 317.8e$

Reteaching 1-3

1–4. Answers may vary. **5.** -3 **6.** 2 **7.** 3 **8.** -20

Reteaching 1-4

1. -7 **2.** 17 **3.** -3 **4.** -10 **5.** 1 **6.** -3 **7.** -8 **8.** -1
9. -1 **10.** -9 **11.** 1 **12.** 9

Reteaching 1-5

The sign of the answer will vary depending on the numbers the student rolled.
1. ± 160 **2.** ± 32 **3.** ± 9 **4.** ± 56 **5.** ± 10 **6.** ± 5
7. ± 4.2 **8.** ± 12

Reteaching 1-6

1–4. Answers will vary.

Reteaching 1-7

1–4. Answers will vary.

Reteaching 1-8

1. $\begin{bmatrix} -2 & 3 \\ 6 & 1 \end{bmatrix}$ **2.** $\begin{bmatrix} 8 & 15 \\ 12 & 3 \end{bmatrix}$ **3.** $\begin{bmatrix} -2 & 7 & 5 \\ 17 & -1 & -4 \end{bmatrix}$

4. $\begin{bmatrix} 8.9 & -0.2 \\ 7.1 & 10.1 \end{bmatrix}$ **5.** $\begin{bmatrix} -12 \\ -11 \\ 10 \end{bmatrix}$ **6.** $\begin{bmatrix} 1 & 6 & -3 \\ -15 & 13 & -5 \\ 5 & -8 & 1 \end{bmatrix}$

Reteaching 1-9

1. -8 **2.** 9 **3.** 10 **4.** 12 **5.** 49

Chapter 1 Answers (continued)

Practice 1-1: Example Exercises

1. 5 **2.** 5.6 **3.** 8.3 **4.** 6.0 **5.** 10.4 **6.** 9.7 **7.** 6 **8.** 6.3 **9.** 7 **10.** 8.9
11. 6 **12.** 7 **13.** 4 **14.** 2, 8 **15.** 9 **16.** 2.8 **17.** none **18.** 7.5
19. Answers may vary. Sample:

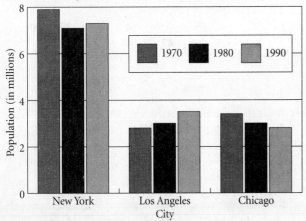

20. New York, Chicago **21.** New York

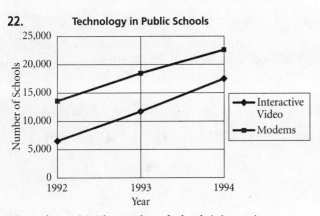

23. modems **24.** The number of schools is increasing.

Practice 1-1: Mixed Exercises

1. 5 **2.** 7.5 **3.** 6.9
4.

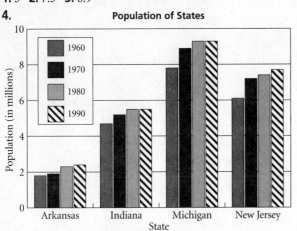

5. It increased from 4,700,000 to 5,500,000. **6.** New Jersey
7. 5 **8.** 4 **9.** 92.5 **10.** 8.25 **11.** 13.4 **12.** 10.5

13.

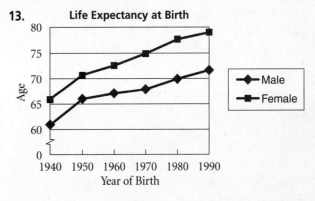

14. Both are increasing. **15.** females **16.** 1940–1950 **17.** 85
18. none **19.** 9.5 **20.** 5.4 **21.** 3.2 **22.** 15.8 **23.** 6.5 **24.** 85.3

Practice 1-2: Example Exercises

1. $c = 1.95b$ **2.** $m = 6.50h$ **3.** $m = 0.05n$ **4.** $c = 10p$
5. $c = 2.50n$ **6a.** c is the total cost and t is the number of
tickets **6b.** $c = 4t$ **6c.** The cost of each ticket is $3.25.
7. Different variables can be used to represent the same value
8. $c = 3.50t$ **9.** $d = 55h$ **10.** $p = 5h$
11. $c = 10 - p$ **12.** $l = 0.45d$ **13.** $r = 500 - t$

Practice 1-2: Mixed Exercises

1. $m = 5n$ **2.** $c = 24.95s$ **3.** $c = 7.50t$ **4.** $p = 7h$
5. $m = 5 - h$ **6.** $g = 30t$ **7.** $m = 0.10d$
8. $n = 48 - g$ **9.** $m = 25g$ **10.** $c = 15 - p$
11. $c = 3.50b$ **12.** $c = 8p$ **13.** $c = 32.95n$
14. $h = 24d$ **15.** $l = 1.25w$ **16.** $e = 250 - s$
17. $p = 0.3s$ **18.** $a = 24 - e$ **19.** $n = 12y$
20a. c represents total cost and g represents number of
gallons. **20b.** $c = 1.25g$

Practice 1-3: Example Exercises

1. $42.75 **2.** $140.35 **3.** 8 **4.** 12 **5.** 22 **6.** 10 **7.** 56 **8.** 2
9. 15 **10.** 18 **11.** 10 **12.** 10 **13.** 42 **14.** 47 **15.** 12
16. 102 **17.** 8 **18.** No; she did not do the division first.
19. 361 **20.** 185 **21.** 704 **22.** 7744 **23.** 3 **24.** 5 **25.** 175
26. 2 **27.** 5 **28.** 2

Practice 1-3: Mixed Exercises

1. 52 **2.** 2 **3.** 65 **4.** 4 **5.** 18.9 **6.** 87 **7.** 13 **8.** 7
9. 2 **10.** 1 **11.** 9 **12.** 12.4 **13.** 19 **14.** 5 **15.** 2 **16.** 6
17. 26 **18.** 29 **19.** 31 **20.** 88 **21.** 14.18 **22.** 85 **23.** 28
24. 7 **25.** 26 **26.** 5 **27.** 55 **28.** 56 **29.** 72 **30.** 24
31. 40 **32.** 2 **33.** 11 **34.** 4 **35.** 33 **36.** 49 **37.** 62
38. 16 **39.** 4 **40.** 12 **41.** 2 **42.** 1 **43.** 26 **44.** $33.95
45. $63.34 **46.** 24 **47.** 2.25 **48.** 4
49. $6 + 8 \div (4 \times 2) = 7$ or $(6 + 8) \div 4 \times 2 = 7$
50. $4 \div (3 + 1) \times 2 = 2$
51. $(5 + 4) \times (3 - 1) = 18$

Practice 1-4: Example Exercises

1. 3.4 **2.** 6 **3.** 11.9 **4.** 3 **5.** $\frac{2}{3}$ **6.** $\frac{4}{9}$ **7.** 2 **8.** -15
9. -14 **10.** -17 **11.** -41 **12.** 5 **13.** 7 **14.** 27 **15.** 42
16. 19.7 **17.** 0 **18.** -16.2 **19.** 33 **20.** 6 **21.** 21
22. -7.6 **23.** -5 **24.** -2.6 **25.** 7 **26.** -16 **27.** -12
28. -8 **29.** 43 **30.** -49 **31.** -21.4 **32.** 14.6 **33.** -9
34. 8.8 **35.** 10.5 **36.** -5.9 **37.** 24 **38.** 17 **39.** -9
40. 26.4 **41.** 12 **42.** -10.6 **43.** 11 **44.** 3 **45.** -3
46. 11 **47.** 19 **48.** -7 **49.** 24 **50.** -4 **51.** 28 **52.** 22
53. -3 **54.** 20

Practice 1-4: Mixed Exercises

1. -28 **2.** -7 **3.** -8 **4.** 13 **5.** 11 **6.** 422 **7.** -15
8. -33 **9.** 3 **10.** 12 **11.** 22 **12.** -18 **13.** 8 **14.** -11
15. -3 **16.** 7 **17.** 16 **18.** -10 **19.** 21 **20.** 9 **21.** -6
22. 10 **23.** -18 **24.** -11 **25.** 5 **26.** -12 **27.** 2.6 **28.** 33
29. -44 **30.** -4 **31.** -0.99 **32.** 11 **33.** 1.9 **34.** 2.4
35. -65 **36.** 5 **37.** 9 **38.** 4 **39.** 12 **40.** -8.86 **41.** 19
42. -18 **43.** 44 **44.** 19 **45.** 20.7 **46.** -1 **47.** 57 **48.** 5
49. 43.2 **50.** 270 **51.** 1.3 **52.** -10 **53.** 6 **54.** 0.88
55. -11 **56.** 6.52 **57.** -7

Practice 1-5: Example Exercises

1. -8 **2.** 69 **3.** -192 **4.** -4 **5.** 210 **6.** -63 **7.** -47
8. -68 **9.** -45 **10.** -32 **11.** -10 **12.** 111 **13.** -37
14. 90 **15.** 0.8 **16.** -30 **17.** 3 **18.** 47 **19.** -3.6
20. -58 **21.** 5 **22.** 1.4 **23.** 8.8 **24.** -0.6 **25.** -4.2
26. -2.8 **27.** 3.8 **28.** -125 **29.** 256 **30.** -16 **31.** 65
32. 27 **33.** -145 **34.** -27 **35.** 24 **36.** -18 **37.** -64
38. 32 **39.** -243 **40.** -8 **41.** -27 **42.** 62 **43.** -16
44. -21 **45.** -432 **46.** 0 **47.** -16 **48.** 576

Practice 1-5: Mixed Exercises

1. -16 **2.** 54 **3.** 81 **4.** -32 **5.** -53 **6.** 196 **7.** 48
8. 20 **9.** -30 **10.** 120 **11.** -49 **12.** -243 **13.** -4
14. -2 **15.** 15 **16.** -125 **17.** 30 **18.** 112 **19.** 343
20. -32 **21.** 49 **22.** -200 **23.** -20 **24.** 256 **25.** -11
26. 32 **27.** 0 **28.** -4 **29.** -42 **30.** 16 **31.** 2 **32.** 91
33. 64 **34.** -120 **35.** -7 **36.** -45 **37.** 64 **38.** -90
39. -5 **40.** -15 **41.** 4 **42.** 72 **43.** -27 **44.** -1019
45. -15 **46.** -4 **47.** 108 **48.** 256 **49.** 2 **50.** -4
51. -5 **52.** 1 **53.** -1 **54.** -2

Practice 1-6: Example Exercises

1. $-\frac{11}{15} > -\frac{4}{5}$ **2.** $\frac{3}{4} < \frac{13}{16}$ **3.** $-\frac{7}{8} < -\frac{4}{5}$
4. $-2\frac{3}{4} > -2.76$ **5.** $-\frac{7}{8}, -\frac{3}{4}, -\frac{2}{3}$ **6.** $-\frac{4}{11}, -\frac{1}{3}, -0.3$
7. $-\frac{5}{6}, -\frac{1}{2}, \frac{1}{3}$ **8.** $-2\frac{3}{4}, -2.7, -2\frac{5}{8}$ **9.** $-\frac{1}{2}$ **10.** $\frac{3}{5}$
11. $-\frac{3}{2}$ **12.** 0 **13.** $\frac{11}{12}$ **14.** $\frac{37}{12}$ **15.** $\frac{11}{12}$ **16.** $\frac{7}{4}$
17. $\frac{13}{21}$ **18.** $\frac{5}{6}$ **19.** 30 **20.** $\frac{17}{2}$ **21.** 9 **22.** -8 **23.** $-10°C$
24. 20°C **25.** $-40°C$ **26.** $-25°C$ **27.** $\frac{8}{3}$ **28.** -7

Practice 1-6: Mixed Exercises

1. $-10.98 > -10.99$ **2.** $-\frac{1}{3} < -0.3$ **3.** $-\frac{1}{2} = -\frac{5}{10}$
4. $-\frac{3}{8} > -\frac{7}{16}$ **5.** $-\frac{9}{20}$ **6.** $\frac{1}{9}$ **7.** -3 **8.** $\frac{7}{3}$ **9.** $-\frac{1}{8}$
10. $\frac{5}{16}$ **11.** $-\frac{5}{9}$ **12.** $\frac{7}{6}$ **13.** -21 **14.** -12 **15.** 12
16. $-\frac{9}{2}$ **17.** 63 **18.** $-\frac{40}{9}$ **19.** $-\frac{8}{9}, -\frac{22}{25}, -\frac{7}{8}$
20. $-3\frac{12}{25}, -3.45, -3\frac{4}{9}$ **21.** $-\frac{1}{3}, -\frac{1}{4}, -\frac{1}{5}$
22. $-1\frac{7}{9}, -1\frac{3}{4}, -1.7$ **23.** $-\frac{1}{3}$ **24.** $-\frac{5}{6}$ **25.** $\frac{4}{3}$
26. $\frac{1}{12}$ **27.** $\frac{3}{4}$ **28.** $\frac{11}{2}$ **29.** $\frac{4}{9}$ **30.** 18 **31.** $\frac{2}{3}$
32. $\frac{10}{3}$ **33.** $\frac{1}{5}$ **34.** $\frac{4}{15}$ **35.** $-30°C$ **36.** 35°C
37. $-35°C$ **38.** 10°C

Practice 1-7: Example Exercises

1. $\frac{1}{50}$ **2.** $\frac{49}{50}$ **3.** 1 **4.** 30 **5.** $\frac{7}{10}$ **6.** $\frac{9}{25}$ **7.** $\frac{17}{50}$
8. 120 **9.** No. The only way to know the exact number
is to test all students.
10–11. Answers may vary. Samples:
10a. $\frac{1}{10}$ **10b.** $\frac{9}{20}$ **10c.** $\frac{11}{20}$ **10d.** $\frac{9}{20}$
11a. $\frac{3}{20}$ **11b.** $\frac{13}{20}$ **11c.** $\frac{3}{20}$ **11d.** $\frac{1}{20}$

Chapter 1 Answers (continued)

Practice 1-7: Mixed Exercises

1–2. Answers may vary. Samples:

1a. $\frac{1}{20}$ 1b. $\frac{13}{20}$ 1c. $\frac{3}{10}$ 1d. $\frac{7}{20}$

2a. $\frac{3}{20}$ 2b. $\frac{7}{20}$ 2c. $\frac{1}{20}$

3. $\frac{4}{7}$ 4. $\frac{2}{7}$ 5. $\frac{5}{7}$ 6. $\frac{4}{25}$ 7. $\frac{3}{25}$ 8. $\frac{12}{25}$ 9. 0

10. $\frac{21}{25}$ 11. $\frac{8}{25}$ 12. $\frac{99}{100}$ 13. $\frac{1}{100}$ 14. 23,760

Practice 1-8: Example Exercises

1. $\begin{bmatrix} -2.4 \\ -7.9 \end{bmatrix}$ 2. $\begin{bmatrix} -2.3 & 4.2 \\ -0.6 & 5.8 \end{bmatrix}$

3. $\begin{bmatrix} -5 & 11 \\ 8 & -1 \end{bmatrix}$ 4. $\begin{bmatrix} -1 & 7 & -4 \\ -1 & -2 & 8 \end{bmatrix}$

5. $\begin{bmatrix} \frac{1}{6} & \frac{3}{4} \\ \frac{1}{2} & \frac{1}{4} \end{bmatrix}$ 6. $\begin{bmatrix} -4 & -1 & -2 \end{bmatrix}$

7. $\begin{bmatrix} 2.6 & -0.6 \\ 5.1 & -0.9 \end{bmatrix}$ 8. $\begin{bmatrix} -1 & 11 \\ -3 & 6 \end{bmatrix}$

9. $\begin{bmatrix} -\frac{8}{5} & \frac{11}{12} \end{bmatrix}$ 10. $\begin{bmatrix} -4 & -7 & 8 \\ 2 & -5 & 9 \end{bmatrix}$

11. $\begin{bmatrix} 8.1 \\ -17.9 \end{bmatrix}$ 12. $\begin{bmatrix} \frac{1}{4} & -\frac{29}{12} \\ \frac{7}{6} & \frac{13}{14} \end{bmatrix}$

13.
Number of Tickets

Performance	Adult	Child	Senior
Matinee	50	40	24
Evening	100	50	36

14.
Olympic Medals

Country	Gold	Silver	Bronze
Kenya	2	4	2
Japan	4	10	13
United States	43	39	39

Practice 1-8: Mixed Exercises

1. $\begin{bmatrix} 3 & 9 \\ -14 & -14 \end{bmatrix}$; $\begin{bmatrix} -7 & -3 \\ 6 & -2 \end{bmatrix}$

2. $\begin{bmatrix} 0 & 3 & -6 \\ 8 & -13 & 1 \end{bmatrix}$; $\begin{bmatrix} 2 & -7 & 12 \\ 0 & -3 & -1 \end{bmatrix}$

3. $\begin{bmatrix} -\frac{17}{15} & \frac{11}{12} \end{bmatrix}$; $\begin{bmatrix} -\frac{7}{15} & \frac{5}{12} \end{bmatrix}$

4.
Population Increase of States

State	Population Increase
Arkansas	500,000
Indiana	1,600,000
Michigan	2,900,000

5. $\begin{bmatrix} -\frac{1}{12} & 4 \end{bmatrix}$ 6. $\begin{bmatrix} -9 & 10.5 & -8 \\ 10 & 5 & -10 \end{bmatrix}$

7. $\begin{bmatrix} \frac{3}{8} & \frac{5}{6} \\ -\frac{3}{20} & \frac{7}{6} \end{bmatrix}$ 8. $\begin{bmatrix} -10 & 10 & -19 \\ -3 & 11 & -1 \\ 10 & -3 & 1 \end{bmatrix}$

9. $\begin{bmatrix} 1.1 & -2.9 & 3.3 \\ -1.4 & -10.9 & 4.2 \\ 0.8 & 0 & 4.4 \end{bmatrix}$

10. $\begin{bmatrix} 140,574 & -11,293 \\ 8228 & -165,327 \\ -84,204 & -40,464 \\ -88,474 & -214,496 \end{bmatrix}$

Practice 1-9: Example Exercises

1.
Cell	Formula
B2	A2 / 2
C2	A2 ^ 2
D2	4 * A2

2.
Cell	Value
B2	1
C2	4
D2	8

3.
Cell	Value
B3	−2
C3	16
D3	−16

4.
Cell	Formula
B2	3 * A2
C2	(A2 + 2) / 3
D2	A2 ^ 3 + 2

Chapter 1 Answers (continued)

5.

Cell	Value
B2	21
C2	3
D2	345

6.

Cell	Value
B3	12
C3	2
D3	66

7a. 12 **7b.** 30.48 **8a.** 29.16 **8b.** 136.89
9a. $8.43 **9b.** $17.23 **10a.** 90 **10b.** 13.6

11.

Name	Pay
Raul	$237.50
Nhan	$296.25
Sue	$249.75

12. D2 + D3 + D4

Practice 1-9: Mixed Exercises

1a. 3.5 **1b.** −11.5

2.

Cell	Formula
B2	A2 ^ 3
C2	(A2 + 4) / 5

3.

Cell	Value
B2	125
C2	1.8

4.

Cell	Value
B3	−1
C3	0.6

5a. 484 **5b.** 16 **5c.** 16
6a. 0.2 * B2 + 0.35 * C2 − 0.45 * D2 **6b.** 93.9; 90.6
7a. 60 **7b.** −20 **8a.** 4.5 **8b.** −0.85

9.

Cell	Formula
B2	A2 / 4
C2	(2 * A2) ^ 2
D2	A2 ^ 2 + A2

10.

Cell	Value
B2	0.5
C2	16
D2	6

11.

Cell	Value
B3	1.5
C3	144
D3	42

✔ Checkpoint 1: For use after 1-5

1. 6 **2.** 16 **3.** 1 **4.** 6 **5.** 5 **6.** 22 **7.** 16 **8.** −9 **9.** −3
10. Positive. Answers may vary. Sample: $(-3)^2$ means −3 times −3 and a negative number times a negative number is positive. **11.** D **12.** $o = 12b$ **13.** $c = 3.50n$

✔ Checkpoint 2: For use after 1-8

1. $\frac{2}{3}$ **2.** −37 **3.** $-\frac{6}{5}$

4. $\begin{bmatrix} 4 & -4 & 5 \\ 10 & -3 & 2 \\ 2 & -5 & -4 \end{bmatrix}$ **5.** $\begin{bmatrix} 1.8 & -11 \\ 10.8 & -0.9 \end{bmatrix}$

6. Answers may vary. Sample: $-\frac{7}{8}, -\frac{1}{2}, -\frac{1}{4}$

7.

Cell	Formula
B2	4 * A2
C2	A2 ^ 3
D2	A2 / 2

8.

Cell	Value
B2	−8
C2	−8
D2	−1

9.

Cell	Value
B3	16
C3	64
D3	2

Chapter Assessment, Form A

1. 1.7, 2, 6 **2.** 90.3, 91.5, 92

3.

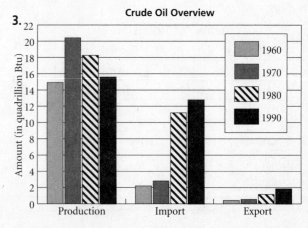

Crude Oil Overview

4. Answers may vary. Sample: The multiple bar graph works best when you are trying to compare amounts.
5. Answers may vary. Sample: This scale works the best with a maximum value of 22 with every two units labeled on the axis.

Chapter 1 Answers (continued)

6. $s = 150m$ **7.** $r = 100 - t$ **8.** \$1050 **9.** B **10.** 20
11. 15 **12.** 16 **13.** -32 **14.** 29 **15.** -16 **16.** 8
17. 32.2 **18.** $-\frac{4}{5}$ **19.** -3

20. $-2\frac{3}{4} > -2\frac{7}{8}$ **21.** $0.23 > \frac{2}{9}$

22. The order of operations was not followed. Division is done before addition.

23. $\begin{bmatrix} 6 & -4 \\ 0 & -10 \end{bmatrix}$ **24.** $\begin{bmatrix} -1.3 & -10.4 \\ 3.1 & 0.1 \\ -0.1 & -0.7 \end{bmatrix}$

25. $2 * (A2 + B2)$ **26.** $C2 = 86$ ft, $C3 = 60.2$ ft, $C4 = 107.8$ ft **27.** $\frac{3}{14}$ **28.** $\frac{1}{2}$ **29.** 36

30. Answers may vary. Sample: $-5 + \left| -4 \right| + 1$

Chapter Assessment, Form B

1. 5, 8, 8 and 9 **2.** 9.6, 9.7, 9.8

3.

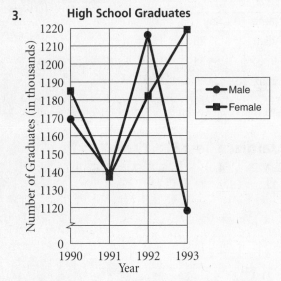

4. Answers may vary. Sample: Use a line graph when you want to see trends. The scale was chosen because the numbers would be easy to graph.

5. $c = 3.45n$ **6.** $r = 162 - p$ **7.** \$51.75 **8.** D **9.** 8
10. -4.4 **11.** -2 **12.** -7 **13.** 0 **14.** 49 **15.** -5
16. -51.4 **17.** $-\frac{6}{7}$ **18.** 5 **19.** $-8.98 < -8.94$

20. $2\frac{5}{11} > 2.45$

21. Answers may vary. Sample: If x is negative, then the left side of the equation is positive and the right side is negative.

22. $\begin{bmatrix} -10 & 30 \\ 16 & -2 \end{bmatrix}$ **23.** $\begin{bmatrix} 3.7 & -3.2 \\ -2.3 & -0.1 \\ 4.7 & -15.3 \end{bmatrix}$

24. $3.14 * A2 \wedge 2$

25. $B2 = 28.3$ ft^2, $B3 = 7.1$ ft^2, $B4 = 211.1$ ft^2

26. $\frac{2}{15}$ **27.** $\frac{3}{5}$ **28.** $\frac{4}{5}$

29. Answers may vary. Sample: 8, 9, 10, 13, 15

Alternative Assessment

TASK 1 Scoring Guide:

3 The response is complete and demonstrates a clear understanding of mean, median, and mode. Data is correctly expressed as percents, with ten scores between 70% and 79%, ten scores in the combined ranges 80–89% and 60–69%, and five scores in the combined ranges 0–59% and 90–100%. The mean, median, and mode are correctly calculated based on the student's data. An appropriate graph is chosen to display the data. The probability is correctly calculated.
2 The answer is mostly correct. Data is correctly chosen, but there are slight errors in calculations. Explanations are clear. The equation for the probability is given correctly, but the result contains slight errors.
1 Data does not fit the distribution correctly. There are serious errors in calculations, or explanations are unclear or incorrect.
0 No attempt is made, or no solution is present.

TASK 2 Scoring Guide:

a. 26 **c.** Answers may vary. Sample: $s = 50n$
3 Both expressions are correctly simplified. Each step is clearly identified and explained. The steps are compared, and explanations show a thorough understanding of grouping symbols, exponents, and order of operations. A new expression is presented and simplified correctly.
2 The answer is mostly correct, but some steps are omitted. A clear explanation is given, but it shows a lesser degree of insight.
1 The response is partially satisfactory, but major steps are omitted. Explanations are incomplete or unclear.
0 No attempt is made, or no solution is present.

TASK 3 Scoring Guide:

Sum is $\begin{bmatrix} 2 & -1 \\ 1.4 & -6.2 \end{bmatrix}$; difference is $\begin{bmatrix} -6 & 11.2 \\ 1.4 & 0.2 \end{bmatrix}$

3 Clear and coherent rules are given. These show a thorough, in-depth understanding of operations using negative integers and rational numbers. Examples are appropriately chosen and clearly support the student's rules. The sum and difference of the two matrices are correctly calculated.

2 Rules are given for most of the operations, with one or two operations omitted or unclear. Examples and matrix calculations are essentially correct, but may contain minor computational errors.

1 Student makes some attempt to write rules and to find the sum and difference of the matrices. Examples are omitted. Matrix operations are not well understood.

0 No attempt is made, or no solution is present.

TASK 4 Scoring Guide:

a. for loan A, total interest = $5,400;
for loan B, total interest = $3,200

3 For each loan, interest calculations are correctly computed and the total amount paid out over time is shown. Regardless of loan selected, a clear and well-organized rationale is presented in favor of one loan over the other. The equation is correct and the variables are identified.

2 There are minor computational errors, but reasoning in support of loan selection is sound. The equation is correct but the variables are not identified.

1 There are major computational errors, and loan selection is not well supported. The equation is incorrect and the variables are not identified.

0 No attempt is made, or no solution is presented.

Cumulative Review

1. D **2.** B **3.** A **4.** B

5.
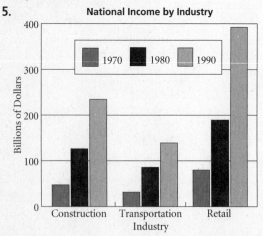
National Income by Industry

6. 14 **7.** -32 **8.** -8 **9.** 24 **10.** -6 **11.** $-\frac{1}{6}$ **12.** 23

13. -15.3 **14.** $-\frac{4}{5}$ **15.** -6 **16.** $\frac{1}{5} < \frac{2}{9}$

17. $-\frac{7}{8} < -\frac{13}{16}$ **18.** $3.6 < 3\frac{2}{3}$

19. $-5\frac{7}{25} < -5.27$

20. $\begin{bmatrix} 3.4 & 0.3 \\ 3.3 & -0.6 \end{bmatrix}$ **21.** $\begin{bmatrix} 6.2 & -10 \\ -2.1 & 4.3 \end{bmatrix}$

22. $\begin{bmatrix} 11 & 3 \\ 1 & 0 \\ -7 & 14 \end{bmatrix}$ **23.** $\begin{bmatrix} -2 & 17 & -1 \\ 4 & 2 & 7 \end{bmatrix}$

24. $c = 1.5n$ **25.** $r = 8 - w$

26a. $\frac{1}{100}$ **26b.** $\frac{99}{100}$ **26c.** 24

26d. Only 200 were actually tested. There is no way of knowing if there will be 2 defective for every 200 in the shipment.

27. B2 * C2

28.

Name	Pay
Adam	$185.25
Jose	$184.38
Franz	$224.00

29. Answers may vary. Sample: 6, 8, 10, 12, 14

Standardized Test Practice

1. A **2.** A **3.** A **4.** B **5.** B **6.** E **7.** B **8.** C **9.** B **10.** A
11. B **12.** A **13.** A **14.** B
15.

```
                    x
          x     x
          x   x   x              x
          x   x   x              x   x
        ──────────────────────────────────
         21  22  23  24  25  26  27
```

mode and median = 22, mean = 23

16. 14 **17.** A4 = (A1 + A2 + A3)/3, 16.2
18. Answers may vary. Sample:

$\begin{bmatrix} 4 & -6 \\ 0 & 9 \end{bmatrix} + \begin{bmatrix} 3 & -2 \\ -1 & 7 \end{bmatrix} = \begin{bmatrix} 7 & -8 \\ -1 & 16 \end{bmatrix}$

19. $\begin{bmatrix} -1 & -2 \\ -1 & 5 \end{bmatrix}$

20. 8 **21.** 9 **22.** -46